D1282976

Half the Fun
Was Getting There

Half the Fun
Was Getting There

by
John Mac Isaac

Prentice-Hall, Inc., Englewood Cliffs, N. J.

Library
I.U.P.
Indiana, Pa.

364.1 M189h
c. 1

Half the Fun Was Getting There, by John Mac Isaac

© 1968 by John Mac Isaac

Copyright under International and Pan American
Copyright Conventions

All rights reserved. No part of this book may be
reproduced in any form or by any means, except for
the inclusion of brief quotations in a review, without permission in writing from the publisher.

Library of Congress Catalog Card Number: 68-25877

Printed in the United States of America • *T*

Prentice-Hall International, Inc., London
Prentice-Hall of Australia, Pty. Ltd., Sydney
Prentice-Hall of Canada, Ltd., Toronto
Prentice-Hall of India Private Ltd., New Delhi
Prentice-Hall of Japan, Inc., Tokyo

Brief portions of this book originally appeared,
in different form, in *Sports Illustrated* and
Mademoiselle.

For a patient and lasting flower. . . .

Half the Fun
Was Getting There

CHAPTER ONE

When the cops finally busted my friend and mentor, Harry Zelnick, it wasn't for the holdups, or the suspected arsons, or the extortions, or for attempting to fix the Detroit Lions football games, or for any of the other respectably criminal things he had been into. They got him for shooting a swan in the middle of Woodward Avenue.

The bird in question belonged to a girl named Leda. That was only her professional name, of course, but everybody called her that all the time, and the regulars around The Brown Bottle Tavern never bothered to think that it might be coincidental. She was just that kinky girl with the snotty bird. And this was not doing full justice to Leda, because she was a very lovely and talented young lady. She and the bird performed in circuses. Not the Ringling Brothers variety, but the sort that specializes in sexually-oriented skits for highly select audiences. She used to come on right behind two Lesbian Wayne State students who were working their way through school by doing intricate things to one another in public. As any trouper will tell you, this is a very tough act to follow. But Leda never lost an audience, and among visiting salesmen, Shriners, and vacationing clergymen she is probably still regarded as one of Detroit's brightest lights, a cultural Mecca second only to the Gaiety Burlesque.

Five or six nights a week, Leda would re-enact the classic affair of Zeus with the original Leda when he appeared in the guise of a swan. She did this stark naked on a lighted platform, stroking and fondling the bird and just carrying on something terrible, until it finally folded its great wings about her and gave every appearance of consummating things. Rumor had it that she practiced her act more often than necessary in the privacy of her apartment, but that was neither here nor there. Leda was an artist, as she always pointed out. She was also a girl of principle — whenever she was called upon to fill in for one of the girls in the Lesbian act she never took any but the passive part.

The trouble started when Leda began bringing her swan with her into The Bottle. In all fairness to Harry, I will say that the bird was a temperamental bastard. Still, it made an effort to get along, and, if guys hadn't kept pouring beer into it, I don't think anything ever would have happened. The bird just couldn't hold its liquor. With only half a bottle of beer in its gizzard, it became surly and downright unneighborly. It tended to monopolize the bar, beating its wings, hissing and honking and scaring hell out of the hustling girls who came in to take a load off their streetworn feet. You have never heard the screeching in your life to match a half-dozen hookers cornered in a back booth by a drunken swan. This always made a big hit with the pimps who congregated in the place — especially when the swan ran right under a table and the girls could only sit there holding their knees together, afraid to get up for fear the bird

2

would snake its head up between their legs as it had been trained to do with Leda. They would sit there cussing and kicking and yelling for Leda to "take this horny son-of-a-bitch home and give it a lay," or "just let this emef get one feather up me and you're payin' triple the standard rate, you bird-lovin' bitch."

This merriment would continue until Leda finally got up and took the horny son-of-a-bitch home with her. Everybody got a good laugh, except the whores and Harry. Harry never laughed much anyway, but he didn't laugh at all about the swan. That was because, right from the beginning, the swan had taken a profound dislike to him and never missed an opportunity to assault or humiliate him.

Harry's hind-end had a way of swallowing up bar stools. When he sat on one, he slopped over so completely that it looked as though the chrome legs were riveted directly to his fanny. That swan could spot Harry's overflow when customers were three-deep at the bar. And, whether it really hated Harry all that much or just had him confused with a cob of Danish Modern corn, it was managing to nip Harry on the average of five times a week. Put him right over the bar every time.

After a while, Harry wouldn't sit on the bar stools anymore. He began sitting at the tables where his overlap would be less conspicuous, but the bird still ferreted him out. Sometimes it would sneak under the table and undo his shoelaces. Or it would nip him on the thigh, just to show what it could do if it really wanted to, and Harry would kick the table over and try to beat the bird to death with a salt shaker. Sometimes the swan would only slip up behind him and nip him, ever so gently, on the ear. That enraged Harry more than all the other indignities combined. It was even more intimate, in a way, than what the bird was doing with

3

the hustling girls. Almost as bad as what it was doing with Leda. And it always gave rise to a storm of ribald observations on Harry's masculinity.

The evening came when Harry could no longer bear the swan's unwholesome affections. He was midway through a fifth of Jack Daniel's when the swan tiptoed beneath the table and took a mighty chop at his left tibia. Harry sprayed sipping whiskey over half the barroom and kicked the table through the front window.

"Alright, you bastard!" he screamed. "You've had it! Ain't nobody pecks Harry Zelnick and gets away with it. I'll fill you so fulla holes, you punk, you'll be able to do your act all by yourself."

With that, Harry whipped out a .45 automatic and began firing.

Everybody in The Bottle dove under a table or took off running, trying to stay clear of the swan and the line of fire. I dove behind the bar where the hustling girls were already six-deep. They were better than sandbags, and I had just forced my way to relative security at the bottom of the pile when the swan made a frantic dash along the top of the bar, hopping and skipping in a most ungainly manner, with Harry hot on its heels. I could hear the rear-door exit slamming as customers fled the premises. The rest of us were pinned down in nooks and corners. Even the restrooms were strained beyond capacity, with mixed crowds seeking shelter beside the commodes.

Leda's swan made five complete circuits of the bar, drawing fire all the way. On the sixth pass, it launched itself through the shattered front window. Harry went through behind it, shoving a new clip into his gun, and the sound of steady firing, panicky honking, and devout cursing could be heard receding in the distance.

4

Harry got his bird three blocks away from The Bottle. The police found him there, in the middle of Woodward Avenue, gloating over the body, still holding the gun. Let me tell you, they racked old Harry with every firearms charge on the books and two or three game-law violations besides. The conglomeration of charges earned him five years in Jackson prison — which, everyone agreed, was a pretty stiff jolt for a fellow who was only trying to save his reputation from a bird. Especially when he didn't really accomplish it. Harry fired 17 shots at that swan, but a Humane Society autopsy later revealed that it had been killed by a ricochet. That kind of shooting didn't help Harry's image up at Jackson any better than having had his ear nibbled by a horny swan.

In a sense, Harry was typical of the people who have made up my world. He was a loser who always lost with a flair and who generally had a good time doing it. His social consciousness was about an inch long, but he always had time to lecture me on the evils of rolling helpless drunks, or swiping Social Security checks from the mail boxes of retirees, or getting jammed up in any of the other petty hustles aimed at people who don't have anything to begin with. "If they ain't got a pot," his favorite saying went, "piss on 'em." Harry was all heart.

And just as Harry was typical of the people, The Bottle was typical of my world. It hosted the improbable and the constitutionally mismatched who were up tight when it came to finding a peer group. And it provided an arena for all the wacky and impossible things that could never happen anyplace else. It was sometimes sad, but more often laughable — because, with a few morbid exceptions, the no man's land beyond the law and the people who inhabit it are a

5

naturally rich source of humor. Perhaps that's why I chose it as my own.

There are those who would flatly denounce my world as a gutter. They are probably right. I will concede the point because I am an expert on gutters. I have been intimate with them — the wide ones and the narrow ones and the deep ones, the deceptively shallow ones where sudden floods are likely to awaken a fellow or even to sweep him down a drain. There are gutters that are never wet and never swept, where the city litter grows ten-feet deep, and a soft, filthy mulch of Wrigley and Hershey wrappers offers lodging to tired citizens. There are gutters that go unfrequented for years and others where you are sure to awaken with a Volkswagen hunkered down on your chest. Some of these gutters offer cheap booze, and some have broads or cards or handbooks or goodly fellows with whom you can plan a quick score. These places are swept out at regular intervals by the police, and if you are hot you might find yourself washed into the sewer of a jail or a prison. But if you are clean — if you are only passing through on your way to something else or on your way to nothing — or if you keep your wits and your sense of humor about you, then you are in a position to enjoy a most revealing view of society. It's a chancy place to tarry, and it can get you into some very bad situations. But, somehow, getting there was always my best game.

The idea is to keep moving and have all the fun you can find. I had a fellow in the next cell, during one of my bad situations at Jackson prison, who was actually born in a penitentiary. His mother, at the time, was serving a five-year sentence for manslaughter. So my friend wound up spending the first few months of his life behind bars.

The authorities finally sprang him to a juvenile home and

6

later tried farming him out to foster homes, but it seldom lasted more than a few weeks; and, between reformatories and prisons, he has probably cost the State of Michigan more money than the Mackinac Bridge. This poor slob was born behind bars, and he has never since felt completely at ease without a few sets of them around him. I've always felt that he received a very shabby deal from life — not because he's spent nearly all of it in prisons, but because he was born to it and was thereby done out of the fun of getting there.

For me, the periodic trips to prison have only been expected, uncomfortable lurches from a 20-year ride on all the fastest roller coasters. And if being locked up hasn't always been much fun, I sure had one swinging ball on the way. It was a different kind of ride, one I took knowing full well that I could get off any time I chose and bury myself in a lot of nice, safe respectability. But I never quite nerved myself up to turning honest.

During the course of my larcenous career, I picked up a broad education in many areas of life that are completely alien to the ordinary, bored-stiff citizen. I worked confidence rackets, I swindled gambling establishments, and, with varying degrees of success, I also doubled as a burglar, safe cracker, car thief, armed robber, and you name it. My companions have been pimps, murderers, addicts, sexual inverts, cops, whores, petty hustlers, dips, assorted nuts, politicians, and thieves in general. I found their company far more interesting and rewarding than anything I might have run into down at the Rotary Club or at the YMCA.

Harry Zelnick, you see, wasn't any sort of anomaly around The Bottle. If anything, he was a trifle sedate compared to the others. There was his girl friend, for instance, a freakish number named Ruthie who kept her head shaved bald as an egg. To keep the wind and weather off, she wore

7

an Egyptian wig that was given to her by another girl who hung out at The Bottle, a stripper named Ethel. Ethel used to do a dance routine in a costume consisting of the wig and three stuffed asps. It was a very exotic number. Two of the asps concealed a nipple apiece in their mouths, while the third appeared to be crawling out of her navel — an effect achieved with a heavy application of strong glue. Ethel managed to stay intermittently decent — and within the city ordinances — only so long as she confined herself to gentle bumps. The grinds were something else. So was her sense of humor. She was always making corny remarks about her "aching asp," or asking startled strangers if they thought she could get away with calling her navel her "asp hole." She eventually retired after an enthusiastic drunk in the front row grabbed her by the lower asp and opened her up like a tab-top beer can.

One time I asked Ruthie why she had traded her own richly red hair for Ethel's wig, and she explained that Harry had shaved it all off when he caught her shacked-up with the window washer in their apartment building. At first the wig had just been a temporary measure, but it turned out that both she and Harry were a little queer for it, and a couple of weeks later Harry went out and shoplifted a Remington Electric for her. He was so taken by the antique charms of the wig that he even apologized to the window washer for breaking his legs with the fire tongs. But that's the way Harry was. He always found a little good in everything.

Another habitué of The Bottle in those days was a con artist named Boris Crempenski. Harry had introduced me to him while I was still in high school so that I could pick up a little experience and a few extra dollars by working as a shill on some of his jobs. Usually, though, he worked

8

alone — most often posing as a clergyman to assure the absolute trust of his victims. He was an ungainly hulk of a man, with beetling brows and a jaw like a cigar box. But put him in a black suit and a priest's collar and he was the very soul of rugged reliability. He simply oozed strength and trust and saintliness. And it was not all on the surface. This was his life's work, and he was as well prepared for it as any graduate of a divinity school. During his stretches in Jackson, he had read every work on theology in the prison library. He was a legitimate Bible scholar, versed in every dogma from that of Tennessee snake worshippers to the Jesuits, and he could quote verbatim anyone from St. Augustine to Annie Besant.

Boris was so convincing that he was once able to assume temporary custody of two separate congregations while their spiritual leaders were off tending to business. On Saturdays, he was Rabbi Crempenski at an east-side synagogue; Sundays, he became Pastor Worthington for a shaky little outfit on the west side. During the week, he panted back and forth between the two organizations looking after their bingo games, potluck suppers, and prayer meetings. And he did such a beautiful job of pocketing funds, liquidating property, and cashing checks against the accounts of those good souls that the First Federal damn near padlocked their front doors.

His best hustle, though, was the man-to-man confrontation. Just Boris and one sucker. His favorite place to find them was out at the old Willow Run airport. He used to go out there and stand by the row of vending machines that dispensed flight insurance to nervous passengers. When he spotted one who looked especially nervous, he would rush up to him and press a Saint Christopher medal into his sweaty hand.

9

"God be with you," Boris would say, concern oozing from every word. "May He protect you from the perils of this hazardous journey. May He watch over you and care for you, just as He does for the many expensive charities that my church maintains. We'll all be praying that you come down safely, brother."

There were many variations on this valediction, some of which would have convinced a veteran pilot that it would be safer to go to Cleveland on a pileated woodpecker than in a turboprop. And when Boris finished his lugubrious pitch and turned away with a tear of final farewell in his eye, it was a stouthearted passenger who didn't feel compelled to kick in a little something for the charities and the extra coverage on their policies.

Boris had charities to fit every occasion. He used to pass the hat at Hamtramck bus stops on behalf of Polish war orphans. He solicited in bars and taverns for donations to support paraplegic saloon keepers. He badgered and wheedled and blessed, and on good days he took in more loot than the Archdiocese of Detroit. He never felt the smallest qualm about taking money in the name of charity because he was convinced that his victims, one and all, were either morally corrupt or basically dishonest. As proof of this last assumption, he maintained an extensive collection of no-account checks that the citizens of Detroit had given to him for his charitable works. He also grumped a good deal over having been robbed. He had approached a mark in Cadillac Square one day asking for a small donation to his church's crippled children's fund. The victim looked him over, then asked, ever so apologetically, if he might see some identification. Boris was ready for this, so he smilingly handed over his wallet. The victim checked it, handed it back along with a two-dollar contribution, and went about

10

his business. Only later did Boris discover that the "victim" had removed more than $80 from the wallet.

Boris was sincerely shocked at the man's bad taste. "Can you imagine," he later complained, "that unprincipled bum robbing a man of the cloth?"

Where else but in The Bottle could I have had the rare privilege of meeting and working with such a man as Boris? It could have been no place but there — or along some similar stretch of low curbing that the world has marked off as a gutter. It's only at the bottom that you can find such a splendid diversity of human types who haven't been run through the cooky cutter that imprints people with button-down collars, two-car garages, and 20-year mortgages. Those were things that never seemed to fit in my life. But The Bottle fit just fine. And the transition that took me, quite unrepentant, from the bosom of a respectable and comfortably fixed family into a life of crime seemed a very natural and inevitable thing.

When I was old enough to do it without getting kicked out, I used to sit in The Bottle many a long afternoon, talk-ing with others who had freely chosen crime as a way of life. Some, of course, had obviously been pushed into it by cir-cumstance; the hustling girls who had been hooked on dope and forced to prostitution to support expensive habits and equally expensive pimps, guys who had come from gut holes in the slums, and the ones who had grown up in reform schools. But there were many like me who had normal back-grounds and only decided later in life to try something profitably dishonest. There was Bob Grenard, a drop-out from the University of Michigan's graduate school who had decided he could make more money as a bookie than as a teacher. There was a girl named Maggie who had quit her job as a secretary in order to become a female tout at the

11

Hazel Park Race Track. There were lawyers who couldn't make the bar, doctors who had decided life would be sweeter if they took their own morphine instead of handing it out to patients, and weirdos of every possible coloration.

It was in The Bottle that I met the only itinerant towel boy in the world. Well, there *may* be others. But if there are, they're not admitting it. His name was John Rapstan, and when I talked with him he was working his way around the country for the twelfth time, taking employment only in whorehouses. He'd stay at one for perhaps a month, running errands, lugging linen down to the laundry, and keeping each girl's room supplied with crisply fresh towels. Professional towel boys being none too common, I asked him about his peculiar choice of occupation. He explained that he was not really so much a towel boy as he was a hobo. And he went on to point out carefully that a hobo was a working man who liked to travel, as opposed to a tramp who liked to travel but didn't like to work, or a bum who did nothing but sit on his dead ass. And it just happened that he was working in whorehouses because, for an unskilled worker in his middle fifties, the wages paid by the madams and the tips handed out by the girls amounted to far more than he could have made sweeping floors in a factory.

The only luggage he ever carried was a black satchel containing a large pair of medical forceps that he used for handling soiled towels. I could see that he was a fastidious man, and I was impressed by this. But I was more impressed by his system for changing jobs. After he had been working in a house for a few weeks and the local scenery had begun to pall on him, he would pack up his forceps and present himself to the madam in charge. Without exception, these tough-minded old broads would take time out from their

12

many duties and charitable works to write him a letter of recommendation.

References for the position of towel boy struck me as being just about the damnedest thing I'd ever heard of. But it wasn't really so unreasonable. Towel boys occupy positions offering considerable temptation, from the standpoint of both cash and merchandise. And most madams select their towel boys with all the care of a prioress picking out a gardener for her nunnery.

John took me into his confidence enough to show me the letter that had gained him his current job. It read:

> Dear Ethel.
> The guy who give you this lettr is alrite people.
> His name is John and he work for me 5 week. He
> didn't swing with nuthing and he didn't bother
> the girls or mess with the johns. He take care of
> the sheats an towels and he allways bring back all
> the change from the lawndary. He ain't on junk
> and he ain't queer. Give him a job for a whil.
> Your friend, Gertrude L.

I don't know who Gertrude was, but I think she should have had an award for being direct and to the point. I've had letters from magazine editors that didn't cover things that nicely. I told John I thought it was very high praise and, if I was running a cat house, I would have hired him on the spot. The letter was so impressive, in fact, that I offered to buy it for five dollars. Our names being the same, it would have made an interesting display to hang up beside my high school diploma. Besides, a fellow never knows when he might need another job. But John was quite indignant at the offer.

"That," he said, "would be dishonest."

13

CHAPTER TWO

    To the ordinary citizen, it may seem odd that people engaged in illegal occupations should concern themselves with the finer points of honesty. It seems to be one of life's paradoxes, though, that the more thoroughly dishonest a person is, the more aware he becomes of honesty as a condition of existence. He knows it as the antithesis of what he is. He depends upon finding it in others to make his living. From all sides he is beset by the forces of it — attempting to reform him, to take vengeance on him, to thwart him, to punish him. And, from time to time, he is even tempted to give it a try. But that is not so easy.

    As proof of the impossibility of turning honest, Boris Crempenski told me a story, one rainy afternoon in The Bottle, in which he compared crime to a tiger. And he told me about a typical Ex-con who was riding that tiger for all it was worth. His limited control over the beast was effected by means of a tight, two-fisted grip on its short hairs. Even with that, he was able to guide their mutual direction by only the smallest degree. And his most diligent efforts were not enough to prevent the tiger from taking an occasional nip out of his leg. Needless to say, the tiger found these morsels both tasty and encouraging.

One day the Ex-con rode his tiger into a Turning Point where an Honest Citizen was standing. This Citizen was endowed with all the usual virtues: social conscience, civic responsibjlity, and a great well of empathy. After sizing up the situation for a moment, he said, "I see that you are riding a tiger," thus demonstrating his keen insight into the problems of the law breaker. At that moment, the tiger turned and took another bite from the Ex-con's leg.

The Citizen regarded this action with a solemn expression and then observed, "My good fellow, that tiger is biting you, and someday he will eat you like a bowl of kippered cod. That is, unless you have sense enough to follow my advice."

"Ah," said the Ex-con, "you know about riding tigers, then?"

"Not exactly," replied the Citizen, "but I have made an extensive study of kittens in general, and I'm quite sure the principles are the same."

The Ex-con pondered this statement with great respect because he had heard of honestly concerned citizens and stood in considerable awe of them. He was able to give only a portion of his attention to the statement, however, being much absorbed in his efforts to control the tiger. Since things were going rather badly at the moment — a state of affairs sometimes experienced when riding tigers — there appeared nothing to lose by accepting the Citizen's aid. "Fine," he said, "climb on and give me a hand."

"Now wait a minute," said the Citizen. "I don't want to get actively mixed up in this, or to dash into things hap-

15

hazardly. But I can assure you it's utterly impossible to live with such a surly beast as you have there. All you have to do is step down."

The Ex-con could see a certain amount of wisdom in that, but the tiger he was riding was the only one he had, and he was loath to let it go. On top of that, he was more than a little afraid that getting off wouldn't be quite so simple. As he pondered this problem, he relaxed his grip a trifle.

"Chomp," said the tiger.

"C'mon, c'mon!" yelled the Ex-con, firming up his hold. "If you want to help me off this son-of-a-bitch, come over here and give me a hand."

"Sorry," the Citizen said, "but I am committed to the over-all field of cats, and I can't afford to get involved with individual cases. However, I have a book written by a group of men who have all the answers: criminologists, psychologists, sociologists, theologists, and quite a number of others. Their advice should be invaluable to you. Here, catch."

The Ex-con reached for the book, momentarily loosening his grip in the process. The tiger promptly turned and ate him like a bowl of kippered cod.

I've thought about that a lot over the years, and I've found enough truth in it so that I could probably build a fairly solid case against turning honest, squaring up, or otherwise setting one's tiger adrift. Relatively few thieves — and I mean *real* thieves, men who have consistently devoted any substantial part of their lives to dishonest pursuits — ever give up the game. I have known a few who tried it, and the results were disappointing, to say the very wretched least.

Because of a belated attempt at squaring up, a friend of mine, named Paul Johnson, ended his days under the unappetizing alias of John Doe in a Cleveland potter's field. He was in his late 30's when he died and had never been arrested in his life. Not even for suspicion. A remarkable feat, really, when you consider that he had been a petty thief for at least 20 of his years. He made his living strictly on short scores — plugging pay phones, a bit of judicious shoplifting, snatching purses or anything else left untended for two blinks, and by filling in with a little con work in seedy bars. He only took small amounts, not because he was petty of soul but because he was basically goodhearted and didn't want to do irreparable financial damage to any of his victims.

One Christmas, a few years ago, Paul and a friend were walking along a deserted street late at night in Cleveland when they came upon a bell-ringing Santa Claus right out in the middle of nowhere. So they stood for a moment in a doorway and watched Santa ring his big, brass bell to the empty streets. Paul was interested in the money pot that hung from a tripod next to Santa. He undoubtedly could have made a bigger score that evening by rolling a drunk, but there was something about money in a pot that fascinated Paul — childhood cookie jar associations, perhaps, or thoughts of glittering heaps of gold at the far end of a rainbow. Anyway, he decided to cop the pot.

Leaving his friend in the doorway to trip Santa should he give chase, Paul strolled over and latched onto the pot. He had it half off its hook when something came over him. He seemed to falter, then just stood there holding the handle. His friend could see Santa pleading with Paul, exhorting him to honesty and probably enumerating all the good works for which the pot was destined. Paul was listening to him and, at the same time, to the Christmas carols that spilled into the street from a loudspeaker over a Rexall drug store.

17

Finally, Paul appeared to have been won over to the ways of righteousness. He released his grip on pot, self, and tiger. And as he turned away with a beatific smile on his idiot face, Santa stepped up behind him and wrapped that brass bell smack around the back of his skull.

Paul was an honest man, dead before he hit the ground.

I knew another fellow, an old syndicate man from Detroit, nicknamed Poppy after the flower that had provided a major source of his revenue. He was a hang-over from the golden generation of the Mafia that is now nothing but a dying rump of the splendid organization it once was — only a lot of old men with old hates who go about planting infernal machines in each other's Cadillacs. It was all getting to be a bit much for Poppy. He was tired of the constant hassling with grand juries, prosecutors, and his fellow countrymen from sunny Sicily. One day he simply decided that he was too old to be shotgunned to death, so he upped stakes and headed for Florida, leaving no forwarding address for his former associates.

Poppy bought a beautiful home in Miami. He abandoned Catholicism and bought himself a deaconship in a small Baptist church. He became a supporter of local charities. He deserted all political interests along with his other criminal activities. He sponsored a troop of Boy Scouts. He adopted a Mongoloid idiot in Pakistan through the Foster Parents' Plan. He made substantial contributions to a civic theater organization. He knitted doilies for a senior citizens' retirement home. He joined the Kiwanis Club. He became a rigidly perpendicular pillar of respectability.

His only personal indulgence was an elaborate aviary. At a cost of nearly $25,000, he constructed a huge glass and screen contraption adjoining his home. This he stocked with an imported jungle of rare plants, and he made it a home for

18

200 hummingbirds from all over the world. This was Poppy's refuge, far away from jails and bombs and cement underwear, a place where he could relax and forget the nagging fears of gangland vengeance and unquashed indictments.

Late one evening, Poppy strolled out into his aviary to forget all these things. Unfamiliar as he was with the flighty ways of birds, he wandered through his imported jungle, crunching over thickets of fern, tugging on vines, rocking the orchids, ruffling the bushes, and setting off storms of panic in 200 hummingbird hearts. Before long, the aviary was a near-silent storm of terror-stricken hummingbirds, darting straight up and straight down, forward and even backwards, as is the way with hummingbirds when they are riled up over their orchids being rocked. Normally, a hummingbird flies backwards no more than a few inches — just far enough to remove its long bill from the heart of a flower — because it cannot see very well in reverse and it could likely back into someone's power mower. As fate would have it, however, one of Poppy's birds flew backwards in the darkness directly into an Amazonian thorn bush. Rudely stabbed from behind, the bird's panic increased immeasurably, and the maddened creature took off across the aviary at full hum. It struck Poppy in the throat like a dart, skewering his windpipe and rendering him breathless. Permanently.

What hidden bombs and hired assassins had not been able to accomplish, belated honesty had not been able to prevent. Poppy's tiger had caught up with him. And it probably would have been no consolation for him to know that the hummingbird had died of a broken neck.

But most of us never make the effort of a Paul Johnson or a Poppy. There is just no inducement for it. Honesty can

19

seem a very pallid way of life after a man has once tasted successfully of crime. He may spend years wrapped up in a drab respectability, working contentedly as a junior assistant bookkeeper until one day, in a moment of weakness or economic despair, he ruptures his tidy little life by dipping into someone else's cash. Suddenly, there is fear in his life, a taste of adventure, and he discovers that he is the owner of an adrenal gland. Gonads, even. He gains a sense of boldness and a dawning knowledge that he has cut himself off from the ordinary world he has been living in for so long. And, in spite of misgivings and the gnawing apprehension of apprehension, he is apt to like it. There are few enough places in the world today where a man can find real frontiers and sure-enough adventure, where he can gamble his wits and freedom against a powerful and implacable authority; few enough ways to lift himself above the banality of a commuter culture or to relieve himself of the burden of pretending to be honest.

And who, after all, *is* honest? Dishonesty and deception are the very cornerstones of our society. They keep the workman from being fired for sloth. They induce people to buy sleazy products for which they have no use, thereby maintaining the economy. They keep husbands and wives from murdering one another — in many instances. They keep judges on the bench when they are too senile to discriminate between sugar and salt. They convince our children that they have had an education after 12 years of sandbox and driver's training. They even move lusty young men with healthy appetites to expose themselves indecently to the mutilations of Claymore mines.

Competent dishonesty is probably the only means to survival in our society. There are many of us who have been sent to prison for clumsy dishonesties. I've known men who

20

spent 50 years behind bars, and others who were hanged, gassed, or electrocuted. But these sentences were nothing compared to the one that would be handed out to a truly honest man. And his fate would be inevitable, as he would certainly be caught. For him alone our legislatures would create new crimes, enact new punishments, devise new tortures more exquisitely refined than anything penology now has to offer. His life sentence would only be a brief detention, the gas chamber an oxygen tent, the rope a soothing chiropractic treatment, the electric chair a pleasant stimulant. Oh, I tell you, they *would* find something devilish for the man who said what he thought and did what he believed.

And the jerk would have every bit of it coming to him, because one spark of pure honesty in this world of ours could well destroy us all.

CHAPTER THREE

The Detroit River, in its own passive way, has done a wonderful job of adapting itself to the city. When I was a kid, you could actually swim in it. We used to sneak onto the Boblo Boat and let the crew chase us right off into the water. Sometimes we just jumped bare-assed from the pilings down by the Vernor's plant until the cops rousted us. And we never thought a thing of getting a mouthful of water because back in those days it *was* water. But the stuff that flows there today would puke the proverbial snipe. The river is a black and stinking gut, littered with bobbing bottles, rubbery blobs of Malthusian refuse, and other, less pleasant articles. It coats the old pilings with bilious scum, and the open channel glistens with the deadly excreta of 10,000 factories. An occasional fish can be seen in this gantlet, holding its nostrils with one fin and fending off what might be called undeactivated sludge with the other, as it dashes frantically from the pollution of Lake Erie to the relative safety of Lake St. Clair. Few of these refugees ever complete their

journey. Their bloated white bellies only add to the loathsome litter on the surface of the waters.

And that is just about the way it's gone with crime. When
I started stealing, there were still plenty of legitimate thieves
taking off proper scores; professionals who worked at their
chosen specialties and adhered somewhat to a code of
ethics. Or at least they exercised a degree of common sense.
But the last few years have brought about a great change.
The ranks of the professionals have been badly polluted by
an influx of what might be called undeactivated sludge —
muggers, strong-arm artists, and idiots who think the only
way to pull an armed robbery is to shoot a cab driver or a
grocery store clerk. Just about everything has gotten worse.

There is one area of crime, however, that has not degen-
erated in even the smallest degree — because it started out
funky and has been that way ever since. I am referring to
the second oldest profession, that of the pimp. And I
wouldn't dignify the hustle with a mention if a young lady
who went by the name of Five-finger Annie hadn't once invited me to become her business manager.

I was more or less between jobs at the time. Boris was
out of town, Harry didn't have anything going, and I was
up tight for a hustle. And that's when Annie, who was more
or less between pimps, offered to share her earnings with
me. I could have used the money, alright, and I was sorely
tempted to accept. But I had always hated to see that sort
of an arrangement, and I had always felt sorry for the girls
who turned over all their earnings to a greasy slob who was
too lazy to work and too stupid and cowardly to steal. The
pimps got the money, and the girls got the spirochetes and
the dope habits and the beatings. It was a stinking system
and, even though I was deeply touched by Annie's offer, I
couldn't bring myself to become a part of it.

Besides, I'd never had much faith in the intelligence of pimps. My low opinion of their capabilities was formed many years ago by the first pimp I ever knew. This was a scruffy little man who used to peddle his wife in the vicinity of Cass Tech High School, an institution that was temporarily suffering my sporadic attendance at the time. I used to see him around the neighborhood, and occasionally I would stop to talk with him and listen wide-eyed to his tales of ill-gotten wealth. When I was lucky enough to catch him while he was still on his first bottle of the day, he would discourse at great length on the stupidity of his customers; suckers, one and all. Marks just begging to be trimmed in both respects.

As sorry a specimen as this fellow was, I was boyishly impressed by his worldliness. And his obvious ability to live without working by separating suckers from their cash was nothing short of admirable. At least it was until I saw him on the job one night. He was standing outside a cheap hotel on Three Street. A cold autumn rain was drizzling down on him, and he looked like a soggy sewer rat.

"Why're you standing out in this mess," I asked him.

"My broad's upstairs with a mark," he explained. "She'll be down in an hour or so, an' I wanna make sure she don't get gay with the dough."

His broad, I'd learned by then, was a five-dollar trick. And while he stood in the rain for two hours, the "sucker" was spending a most enjoyable evening in a warm, dry bed. I wasn't the brightest kid who had ever been kicked out of half the high schools in Detroit, but I did know a moral when I saw it standing all sodden in the rain.

I've never met a pimp who cared about people. And, from that standpoint, they are more dishonest, more totally corrupt and devoid of conscience than any thief who ever

24

Library
I.U.P.
Indiana, Pa.

364.1 M189h
c. 1

robbed a poor box. Because a thief only takes money. And money, after all, is not such an important thing. Money can always be replaced. So it's not just taking money from a woman that makes a pimp a swine; it's robbing her of the last vestiges of human warmth, defaulting on the fulfillment of the needs that drove her to him in the first place. Because a hooker who supports a pimp is a woman who needs a man she can call her own so badly that she will accept any sort of vermin into her life and into her body. And there isn't a pimp going who will give a girl a fair shake on a deal like that.

If pimps are pure Dreck, however, whores are generally pretty good people. And I've known enough prostitutes in my time to stock every house from Houston to Hong Kong. They live in a clannish little world of their own, but once they catch on that you're not going to take their earnings away from them or preach to them it's hard to find a more interesting and diverse group of companions. I used to pass a lot of time talking with the Hatrack types who flocked into The Bottle every afternoon, and the way they cut up the johns, ran down the pimps, and described the idosyncrasies of their customers was better than any floor show in town.

Still, there was the necessity of finding some sort of a hustle to keep myself going — preferably something more acceptable to my young scruples than living off the earnings of a prostitute. So I looked up a fellow named Arnold Roth, a rather unlovely type who had once offered to turn me into a first-class Murphy man. This didn't speak well for my scruples, since a Murphy man is really nothing more than a pimp without a product. But the distinction was enough to satisfy me at the time. And, fortunately, I have a happy tal-

25

ent for staying ahead of such rationalizations; by the time I get around to questioning an unjustified distinction I have usually managed to overcome the scruples that gave birth to it.

Arnold Roth was a two-bit grifter whose greatest asset was his oily and obsequious manner. He was a small man with a taste for checked coats and alligator shoes. He garnished his lip with a pencil-line mustache, the kind that would have guaranteed him a job as an extra in anybody's grade B poolroom movie. And he not only looked like a legitimate pimp, he conscientiously exaggerated the traditional characteristics to the extent that he almost walked sideways. It wasn't easy to like Arnie, but you had to give him credit for knowing his work. He was so thorough about it that he even invented little touches of his own, like carrying a wallet full of pin-up photos that he'd had copied out of Playboy. These were "his" girls — perfect bait for a wavering sucker.

I followed Arnie around for two nights, watching him do the Murphy-man bit. The idea of the thing was to find a john who was looking for a little action, then to convince him that you had a girl who could furnish it. Arnie accomplished this by sidling up to everyone who didn't look like a cop and muttering something enticing.

Like:

"Hiya, pal. You lookin' for a little fun tonight?"

Or:

"Say, buddy, I got a beautiful broad over at the Hamilton House who's real lonesome for a big fella like you."

That sort of thing, you know. I winced at every hackneyed approach he made, but the time-worn gambits seemed to be the ones expected by the johns, and a surprising number of them evinced a lively interest in the imaginary broad over at the Hamilton House.

When he finally had the john all sewed up and drooling over the gallery in his wallet, Arnie would let him select the girl he wanted for the evening and then give him a Hamilton House room number with no more substance than the girl. The fee for this service ranged between five and 25 dollars, depending on the eagerness and the affluence of the mark.

Arnie was always careful to instill in his victims a feeling of trust. He accepted his fee almost with reluctance, as though he were engaged in this occupation only as an humanitarian service to the sexually undernourished. And when he tucked the cash away, it was always with the pious admonition, "Now, you've already paid for your fun. Don't let that dumb broad ask you for no more dough. Just tell her I sent ya and go ahead and do whatever you want with her."

The whole thing seemed to work beautifully. There were also some obvious advantages, not the least of which was that the cops couldn't nail you for pandering because there wasn't really any girl. And not having to work with a girl was an advantage in itself, since you didn't have to worry about her getting jealous or teed-off about some little thing and blowing the whistle on you. For a while, this had all the earmarks of turning into my life's work — short hours, good money, and the worst charge I could ever get out of it was Larceny by Trick; a misdemeanor, if you please.

I soon found out, however, that I didn't have Arnie's flair for the profession. Perhaps I lacked the common touch. Anyway, I didn't exactly do a thriving business. During my first week as a Murphy man I cleared the magnificent sum of $62.25. The odd two bits came from a clown who told me to go out and treat myself to some of my own wares.

But, in a way, I did manage to distinguish myself in the

27

trade by beating a mark and giving him his money's worth at the same time. I brought about this paradox one evening on Woodward Avenue when I spotted a bright-eyed little man in a trench coat who had "The Look" about him. The Look is something you learn to watch for in this business. It's an aura, really. A tense, eager, and myopic sort of thing about a person that tells you he is apt to be receptive to an interlude of forbidden pleasure. It's quite similar to the open-mouthed look of credulity that a con man is always watching for. There is no trick to it. It's just a question of cultivating a sensitivity to people's weaknesses.

My man in the trench coat showed strong signs of every imaginable weakness, plus a few that might have been beyond normal comprehension. Not that it mattered much what his action was. As live as he looked, I was fully prepared, in my capacity as Murphy man, to promise him an apartment full of live octopi. It turned out, however, that he was willing to settle for a woman.

Since he was one of the shrewd types who won't part with their money too far in advance, I walked him down the street to an apartment building called the Duncan Arms. There I gave him a reassuring pat on the shoulder and rang the buzzer for apartment 369 in a pattern of dots and dashes that would look like a prearranged signal. I chose 369 at random because it sounded like a nice, progressive number, not to mention temptingly lascivious in the penult and ultimate. Luckily, someone was home. When the lock on the foyer door hummed open, I relieved the mark of his ten dollars and aimed him at the stairs. The last I saw of him, he was burbling happily and stumbling in his eagerness to get up to his party in 369.

Now, a strict rule for any successful Murphy man is to stay out of a client's way for at least a couple of days. There

28

aren't many of them who would ever intentionally turn you in to the cops as most are the squarest of johns: family men, guys in business, ministers, things like that. They don't want any scandal. But if they run into you right away, their angry frustration is apt to boil over in spite of their better judgment. They want to jump on you, or ask a lot of silly questions. And they always expect you to give them their money back.

It hadn't been more than an hour since I'd dumped this creep in the Duncan Arms. I was standing outside a restaurant nearly six blocks away, discussing the subtleties of our business with Arnie, when I saw him coming. His tie was undone, the buttons were torn from his trench coat, and his hair was hanging damply over his eyes.

"There you are," he yelled from down the street. "Hold on a minute. I've been looking all over for you."

That figured well enough. This was the worst possible disaster. The jerk must have walked into that apartment and tried to climb in bed with somebody's wife. From the look of him, I figured the husband must have been at least a weight lifter or a construction worker. Hell, as torn up as he looked, he might have tried to climb in bed with the husband.

"Arnie," I said, "stall this guy. I don't know how the hell he found me, but I just burned him over at the Duncan Arms. He might have a gun."

"Naw," he said, "these guys never got heat. Just stick around, kid, and I'll show ya how to cool him. I guarantee it, I'll get another ten out of him and dump him in the Book Cadillac."

By this time the mark, panting heavily, was right on top of us. So I put on an expression which I hoped conveyed the

29

image of an honest businessman who had just made a small, but regrettable, error in the apartment number.

"Friend," I began, "I was just telling old Arnie here that I thought I might have made a small. . . ."

"Lemme tell you first," he interrupted. "That was the best deal I ever made in my life for ten dollars."

"It was?"

"Lemme tell you it was! That girl knew things I never even thought of."

"She did?"

"Lemme tell you she did! Boy, was she ever something. Anyway, I said to myself, if you could steer me onto one broad like that, chances were you knew a whole lot more of them, huh?"

"Yeah, sure," I said. "Lots and lots of them. . . . Lots."

"Buddy, you just don't know all the things she did to me. Are the others just as good?"

"Better," I said, counting the hickies that ran down his neck and could be seen trailing on down across his solar plexus where the buttons had been ripped from his shirt.

"Man," he said, "that action with the fruit bowl! Who ever heard of a kick like that? It was terrific!"

I couldn't believe this creep was for real. He'd actually gotten himself laid up there — or something. A fruit bowl? Arnie was looking at me as though I'd betrayed the profession. If the creep had him convinced, that was good enough for me.

"Look, pal," I said, clapping him amiably on the shoulder. "I haven't seen our lady friend for a couple of days and she changes hair dye about every four hours. How's she looking tonight?"

"Kind of a tawny blonde, if you know what I mean. She had it all piled up on top of her head, but she let it down when she went to work. Hung clear down to her can, it did."

"You just knocked and she let you in?"

"Sure. What else? 'Your man sent me up for a little action,' I said, and she told me to come on in."

"Good. Good," I said, "that's just the way I told her to handle it. Well, if you'll excuse me, now, old Arnie and I have some business to take care of. But you just look me up any time."

I grabbed Arnie by the arm and hauled him off with me in the direction of the Duncan Arms. I was curious as hell, and I think the fruit bowl bit had Arnie hooked.

Behind us, the mark called out, "On second thought, forget about those other broads. Just fix me up with the same one tomorrow night."

Arnie and I broke into a trot.

Number 369 in the Duncan Arms looked the same as all the other apartments, but there was mystery behind that closed door. What strange spider must have spun its web in there so that a dumb slob in a trench coat could run in on a hummer and get ten times his money's worth? There was a woman in there with long, tawny hair? There was a fruit bowl? I dug Arnie in the ribs and he knocked.

We heard steps inside. The door opened. The woman who opened it could have been anyplace between 30 and 40. She had on a blue satin wrap which left little doubt that she was in excellent condition, whatever her age. Her hair was a tawny blonde and it hung clear down to her can.

"So you're the ones," she said, "who sent that poor little schmuck up here. I might have expected it of you, Arnie, but not him."

And that's how I first came to know Marlene Regis, shill deluxe, stripper, bonne vivante, good people, and a magnificent whore. She was an old friend of Arnie's, and I'd seen

31

her a few nights around the clubs, but all I knew about her at the time was that she was tied up with rackets people. Actually, she was one of the most extraordinary people I've ever known. At the age of ten, she had left her virginity with an old gentleman in Wilkes-Barre and struck out on her own with a crisp five-dollar bill in her pocket. At 15, she was caught, flagrante delicto, with a bishop. At 20, she was the main attraction at all upper-class stag parties in Chicago — her specialty was being served up on a silver platter, her nude body smothered in anchovy sauce. Ah, lovely Marlene, with her fine sense of the ridiculous and her taste for the bizarre. I eventually took her with me on a check-cashing spree and we got to know one another quite well — although she never would explain about the fruit bowl. But more about that later.

And that's how, purely by accident, I almost, but not quite, became a legitimate pimp.

CHAPTER FOUR

It's impossible to live for any length of time a life such as I was living without landing in jail — at the very least. I landed there frequently. My first jail beef came when I was 18. I drew 30 days for slugging a cop who got snotty about the ID I was using in a bar. I acted as my own defense attorney in the case, maintaining, as I recall, that I had mistaken the policeman for a British naval officer. That was the first case I lost and the first time I went behind bars.

There were many jails after that one. There were jails for minor offenses, jails for suspicion, jails awaiting transfer to the penitentiary, and jails for GP. That last category is a very common one when you already have a record. It means getting pinched on general principles for such hypothetical crimes as Mopery in the Third Degree. It means the cops just want to give you a hard time, or they want you to get out of town, or they are peeved because one of their quaintly fascistic little hustles fell through, or even that they are bored.

But jail time is usually short time, and I never minded it too much. In most cases I had so much fun getting myself arrested that the confinement provided nothing more punitive than a chance to recuperate. And I was always able to learn something new. My experience in county jails formed the basis of an extensive liberal education in many areas essential to survival. Within their dank confines I've learned the finer points of smuggling, subornation, starvation, and a host of subjects almost too arcane to be recognized as legitimate fields of study by those who have not undergone similar experiences.

It was my jail time, for example, that allowed me to carry out extensive research on the burning qualities of various papers. Cigarettes are at a premium in most of these places, and the first thing you learn when you are tossed in a cell is never to throw a butt in the toilet. It makes them, as Shakespeare points out, soggy and hard to light.

To assure yourself a steady supply of smokes, you have to save every last grain of tobacco against such eventualities as running out of money, as you are certain to do under all but the most honest administrations, or incurring the disfavor of the head turnkey, which you are also certain to do unless you happen to be a fink or a vegetable. If a fellow wants to get fancy about it, he can split the butt of a cigarette as soon as he is through smoking it and wrap the tobacco in the cellophane from the original pack. He can even stuff a little something in with it to retain the moisture; a piece of boiled potato does just fine. Since such measures do nothing for the flavor, I have always preferred to allow the butts to cure naturally. It has been my experience that the tobacco separates from the factory papers much more easily when it is bone dry. You may take that for what it's worth.

34

The main problem is finding the proper paper for rolling your retreads once you've saved up enough tobacco. I've tried nearly everything possible in the course of my investigations. Glazed paper, I found, has a tendency to char heavily without burning back. A page from the *National Geographic*, as a matter of fact, will not burn at all once you have extinguished the initial blaze caused by lighting the cigarette. You have to puff constantly to keep the thing going, and the heat build-up is terrific. It's rather like smoking a pipe made from a straight length of copper tubing, an experience guaranteed to scorch the lips and shrivel the nostrils. It is much the same case with all slick magazines. Smoke three cigarettes rolled from *Holiday* or the *Saturday Evening Post* and your eyeballs tend to soften and roll sluggishly in their sockets. And I've known men to bleed from the ears after smoking only a single page from the *Reader's Digest*.

Pulp magazines and plain old newsprint are more satisfactory to the extent that they will burn back almost at the same rate as the tobacco, but there is still a problem of heat conduction, and the stuff tastes like a burning compost heap. Bible paper is quite acceptable for rolling; unfortunately, smokers outnumber Gideons, and the supply is undependable.

The most satisfactory paper, available today in most jails (at least in the north), is ordinary toilet tissue. The paper tends to make a rather limp cigarette — though not so limp as you might suppose, since the tissue supplied in jail has little in common with the effete fluffiness of the product familiar to most people. The only real drawback is that it imparts to the smoke a flavor something akin to toasted marshmallows. Not altogether unpleasant, but it does take some getting used to.

Matches, of course, are almost as scarce as cigarettes in most jails. As often as not, you sit there beady-eyed, watching the flame on your lighter become more and more insubstantial with each day of confinement. Finally, you trade the thing to a trusty or a screw for a book of matches. When things are especially tight, you can't even chance the extravagance of burning an entire match. Instead, you split each match lengthwise through its narrow dimension. Then, if you can get hold of a razor blade, each half is sliced once more, making four matches out of one. You can't dawdle over lighting a cigarette with one of these things, but they work well enough if you have a good set of lungs.

The average American jail, if there really is such a thing, can often provide a better break with reality than a trip on LSD. Many lockups are so far out they hardly seem credible, even while you're in them; wild figments of a senile sheriff's second childhood. It was in a Missouri jail, for instance, that I found myself locked in the same cell with a troup of hootchy-cootchy dancers.

I'd stopped for a red light in this little fester of a community along the highway when the local sheriff ambled over and asked to see my registration. Just like that. I wasn't even violating an ordinance. Sheriffs out that way all dress like Hoot Gibson, and you can't explain a damn thing to them. So I handed him my papers, which he pondered, first one and then the other, for a good five minutes. At each ponder his eyebrows eased a bit higher. It wasn't hard to figure out why. My phony ID was made out in one name and the registration for the car, which I'd borrowed from a friend back in New York, was made out in another.

So I landed in the local jail. This was a one-room cage furnished with two sets of bunk beds and a creaky, leaking old doniker. At least, I thought, there would be plenty of room to stretch out in. As things developed, the place filled up pretty quickly. I seemed to have landed at the peak of the season. Two hours after he turned the key on me, the sheriff of that evangelical backwater, at the behest of ten local preachers (village population: 400), arrested the girly show of a nearby carnival.

I was sitting on one of the bunks, reading a three-year-old *Youth For Christ* magazine, when I heard a key in the lock. Here was *real* salvation, I thought. The sheriff was ready to be bought. Peeking over the top of the magazine, I was stupified to see six females being escorted into the cage. One was wearing a leather jacket and a grass skirt. The others were tastefully decked out in overcoats, and if they had anything under them it certainly didn't show where the buttons were missing.

Those good Missouri citizens who were so worried about the morality of six women shaking their sexual paraphernalia at a crowd of rustic lechers in a carnival tent seemed surprisingly unconcerned about dumping them into my four-bed, one-donicker cell. And perhaps they were right to be unconcerned. During the three days that the seven of us were together, nothing more exciting occurred than a good deal of blushing and mutual embarrassment whenever any of us were forced by overtaxed bladders to make use of the sanitary facility. The rest of the time we played gin rummy with a deck of cards that one of the girls had smuggled in; that provided all of us with a certain amount of satisfaction, since the local clergy considered card playing to be even more wicked and sinful than unblessed copulation.

I should point out, however, that even in our goofed-up county jails such mixed lodging is highly unusual. Every other lockup I've ever been in (here in the United States, anyway) has separated the sexes with glassy-eyed fanaticism, though there are exceptions to this rule. On many occasions it has been badly fractured by both male and female inmates who devoted much single-minded effort to putting things on a more comfortably heterogeneous basis. Sometimes this is done with the cooperation of jailers who can be bribed to make available one of the professional ladies from the women's section. And sometimes it is done without cooperation.

I've seen the time in Detroit's Wayne County Jail when the whole building echoed with the thumping and bumping of traffic through the ventilation ducts that connected the men's section with the women's. When those routes were finally closed off, the inmates took to talking with one another through the commodes. A chap on the fifth floor would splash the water out of his toilet bowl, thereby breaking the water seal, and a girl on the sixth floor would do the same. Then, crouching there with his head in the bowl, whispering endearments through the sewer pipe, he could make whole days flitter by as though they were no more than months.

About the best thing you can say for such an expedient is that it was more romantic than sitting around reading girly magazines. And it was generally more fruitful — my old friend Boris Crempenski met his third wife through those very same plumbing facilities.

But such things as dancing girls and sewer pipes could never really come as any surprise to me. I've run into so many screwball situations and freaky people in the county jails of this country that it wouldn't astonish me to be locked up with anything short of a lemon-lime aardvark.

I was locked up one time with a guy who was wigged out on cockroaches. He had spent so much time in jails in general, and drunk tanks in particular, that he saw roaches even when they weren't there. He talked about nothing else.

"There," he would scream. "That's the scoundrel. Dirty bastard. Show me an insolent insect and I'll show you a cocky roach, I say."

It was his conceit that these insects followed him from jail to jail, pursuing a personal vendetta for some obscure grievance he had committed against them years before in New York City's Tombs. It's hard to imagine what anyone could do to a cockroach to get the whole tribe up in the air like that, but this guy seemed to have managed it. Our little cell was so overrun with the beasts that I almost came to believe his rantings. Whole phalanxes of roaches maneuvered across our walls. They dropped on us from the ceiling, played hide-and-seek in the shadows of the bars, peered malevolently at us from holes in the concrete with glittering, compound eyes. They fought like wolves for the sticky smears on discarded candy wrappers and did strange, roachy things in the folds of our blankets. They were a rum lot, they were.

Having had long experience with this plague, my friend fought back valiantly. He bombarded the little swine with his shoes and flayed them with his belt. Sometimes he squirted lighter fluid on them, and then, not content to watch their gasping and gagging death spasms, he would impatiently throw lighted matches at them. His favorite weapon was the paper clip and rubber band. He was so deadly accurate with these missiles that he could pick off cockroaches on the run at a range of ten feet. An amazing feat; and I can testify to this because I've tried the same thing with flies, without much success.

Our cell took on all the aspects of a battlefield — the booming artillery of my friend's shoes thundering against the walls, the whine of ricocheting paper clips, the fire and smoke of his lighter fluid flame throwers, the blood lust in his eyes, and the reek of death. It was all there. And I don't mind admitting that I sat out most of these skirmishes prudently entrenched in my bunk, beneath two blankets.

As a final touch, perhaps as a gesture of grudging respect for his implacable enemy, my cellmate constructed a Tomb of the Unknown Cockroach. He spent two days chipping old chewing gum from the bottom of his bunk and two more softening it in the sink. And from this unspeakable crud he carefully fashioned a small mausoleum, complete with embossed weeping willows and angels and the whole pantheon of mortuary oddments. He topped it all off with a paper American flag, razor-bladed from *Life* magazine and flown at half-toothpick from the mausoleum's sticky dome.

As numerous as cockroaches may be, probably the most common vermin around jails and penitentiaries are the professional soul collectors who swarm about the newly incarcerated like unwholesomely green and shiny flies on an open wound. They come when the sinner is most vulnerable and repentant. They come with quiet voices, Bibles, tambourines, piety, holy water, insinuations of doom, threats of damnation, sly preachments, religious uniforms, tracts, and pamphlets; colporteurs of perdition floating on the effluvium of grubby religious printing presses, promisers of salvation, adventists, sally anns, faggoty friars, the unity crew, forget-the-man missions, brotherhood incorporated in the body of Christ — they all come running with their hymns and mitres and sermons and all the other weapons of militant Christianity. Thank you, God, for the Buddhists who never bother a poor slob who finds himself torn from the bosom of his loving mistress, stripped of the quiet comforts of the corner fleshpot, and thrown all lumped and bruised into a cold, unloving cell. A pox on the Christians who counsel a stiff upper lip and an ache in the arse.

A notable exception to this general run of professional salvationists was Nelly Simpson. She came with something far more substantial than piety.

Nell was really rather plain, but with a lovely body. Firm and supple. She wasn't overblown in the chest as is so often the case with the stereotype of sensuous women. Her breasts were small but succulent, like those of a Modigliani nude. A willowy cat, otherwise indistinguishable from the horsy herd of female evangelists bearing Christ's standard in the hinterlands of New York State.

I first met her midway through an eight-month county jail sentence. She used to come around every Sunday to talk with the men and to give them Gideon Bibles and a sermon. A turnkey always accompanied her when she made the rounds of the cell block passing out the Bibles and the pious advice on personal problems — "Bless you, my good man, and don't worry about your wife. She'll find someone to look after her while you're away." Or, "Don't be discouraged, young fellow, ten years really isn't such a terribly long time. Why, in the eyes of God it's not even as one second." Then, when she had finished spreading her bit of cheer, damn near starting a riot in the process, Nell would select a couple of trusties to go with her to the little closet just off the mess hall where the public address system was kept. There, while the two inmates played religious recordings on a small record player that never ran at the right speed, and while the guard was forced by the cramped restrictions of the closet to sit outside and cool his heathen heels, Nell would deliver her sermon to the boys in the cells. Among other things.

The second Sunday after Nell selected me to help with

41

the recordings I found out about the other things. Oh, generous and understanding woman. Magua Mater. Fertility goddess. Cybele. Healer of aching souls. While that gump of a turnkey sat outside the door reading comic books, while the other trusty put The Old Rugged Cross on the record player and kept an eye on the gump, dear Nell offered herself up for a most delightful exchange of caresses. Offered? Nay, insisted. Demanded, even. Tender Nell with the sweet, Modigliani breasts and delicious thighs.

It was a wonderful break in the hungry monotony of serving time, but a bit disconcerting that first Sunday because, even in our most intimate moments, Nell went right on with her sermon. Although I did notice a marked increase in volume, I was much too preoccupied for anything like a qualitative analysis. The other trusty, however, later informed me that her harangue had seemed to become increasingly sincere and that her biblical references had shifted to Solomon and his song, which she quoted in its entirety toward the end.

By the time I was released from jail, four months later, there were men in that lockup who had large portions of the Song of Solomon firmly committed to memory.

Years later, way-the-hell-and-gone out in Nebraska, I ran into Nell again. This time, though, I didn't have a chance to exchange prayers with her. The hick fuzz had me locked in an isolation cell because of a few ill-considered remarks I had made on the subject of escape. I was just about half asleep — which is about as far as you can get when you are naked on a concrete floor — when, from the nearby bullpen, I made out the peculiarly unmistakable drone of a sermon. I was doing my best to ignore it when it finally registered that the volume was edging up — and that the text, in that same familiar voice, was from the Song of Solo-

42

mon. The delivery, I noticed, was none too steady. "His left hand is under my. . . . Ohhhh . . . . and his right hand doth embrace me. . . . My beloved is mine, and I am his: he feedeth among the lilies. . . . Ahhhh. . . ."

Dear old Nell! It couldn't be anyone else having religio-sexual orgasms in that tone of scripture. I hadn't ever pictured her as being anyplace except at that same old New York jail, but naturally she would have to move around a lot, leaving behind her a trail of red-faced sheriffs and outraged civic leaders as the nature of her ministrations became known. Poor, driven Nell, who did more for the suffering, locked-up misfits in our jails than all the high-minded cardinals, do-gooder Methodists, and Lesbian social workers put together. That concrete felt almost comfortable, just knowing that Nell was in the next room.

CHAPTER FIVE

After washing out as a Murphy man, I drifted from one job to another and gradually worked my way into the more legitimate areas of crime. I handled a phone in a horse book, I sold phony identification papers, and I picked up spare change by hijacking tires and generators from automotive-parts warehouses. There have always been plenty of such job openings in Detroit, so there was no excuse for a conscientious young thief to go unemployed. I did alright with the hijacking, and I moved up from that to a regular job with a hot car ring. That one lasted eight months, then the law broke things up, and I found myself between jobs again.

I was only out of work a few days before I found another position of trust and responsibility. I became a bag man for Big Pastrami, one of the biggest numbers operators in Detroit. That was not his real name, and he was not even Italian, but everybody called him that because he had a habit of carrying hot pastrami sandwiches around in his pockets. Sometimes they were wrapped in brown paper and sometimes they were not. His pockets were a mess.

Big Pastrami was the classic example of a small-time hoodlum who finally made it big. During Prohibition, he had worked as a muscle mechanic for the Vitale brothers. The brothers brought whiskey across the river from Canada, and Pastrami helped see to it that nobody hijacked the stuff before it was delivered to the Chicago distributors. He was very good at this. When I worked for him, he was already in his 60's, and his greasy suits hung shabbily from a tall and gaunt frame. But during the 20's, he had weighed better than 250 pounds, and he had applied them skillfully wherever the brothers Vitale had directed.

One would-be hijacker who somehow survived a working-over at the hands of Pastrami is employed today at the Ford plant in River Rouge. He runs a semi-automated milling machine that was apparently designed to be handled by an opossum. Every ten minutes, the operator has to wedge himself into a narrow slot on the side of this machine and perform two simultaneous operations. Bending stiffly forward from the waist at a 45-degree angle, he must insinuate his left hand through an aperture to hold down a lever, while with his right hand he depresses a button that is located five inches behind and directly between his shoulder blades. A normal person would be incapable of performing this operation without the aid of a prehensile tail, but our former hijacker performs it with ease. Thanks to the ministrations of Big Pastrami, he has a 45-degree curvature of the spine, and his right arm is permanently locked behind his back in such a position that his hand is situated almost on a level with the nape of his neck. For 40 years, in a forgotten corner of the Rouge plant, he has been pushing that button with as little difficulty as though it were his own navel. All thanks to the genius of Big Pastrami, other men may some day become as happily adapted to their machines.

In 1929, Big Pastrami did a semi-automation job on a Detroit policeman and was sent to prison for Assault with Intent to Maim. By the time he got out Repeal was in, and the Vitale brothers had gone back to peddling fruit. This was much too tame for Pastrami, so he took a job running numbers for a now defunct organization on the east side. It was a fateful move. Although misfortune befell many of Pastrami's associates, his own affairs prospered, and he moved steadily upward in the rackets. Now and then, when one of his immediate superiors was found floating face down in the Detroit River, there would be unkind rumors to the effect that Pastrami was not an honorable man and that he was not the sort of fellow one should go strolling with along the waterfront. But these veiled and groundless accusations meant nothing to him. He continued to take his waterfront strolls, and he continued to move up until he finally controlled the entire east side.

Since he had begun his odyssey of success right at the bottom, just as I was doing, Big Pastrami was quite an inspiration for me. But he was pure slob. There was no getting around that. Not only did his pockets stink, he belched continually, and he spat on the floor of his office with complete disregard for the ten overflowing gaboons that sloshed around his desk. He loved cigars, but not as much as he did the ritual of lighting them. This was associated in his mind with elegance, and he was constantly clipping them in half with a pair of office scissors, lighting them, trimming them, grinding them out on his desktop or throwing them still lighted to the floor where they often started blazes that had to be put out by one of his goons. When lighting a cigar, he had a habit of throwing back his head and exclaiming:

46

"Ah, garfoom!" (His own corruption of the French *par-fum*.) "I tell ya, it's the sweet breath of God blowin' down your throat!"

God with halitosis, maybe, or God breathing through an old sock, but surely not sweet. He ordered those ropes from a discount house run by his cousin in Lebanon, and there was a rumor current among his friends that the stogies contained the shredded bodies of Israeli border guards. If that were true, one sweet puff would have turned Ben-Gurion himself into a raving anti-Semite.

My duties in Big Pastrami's organization were not especially difficult. By its nature, the numbers racket is probably the simplest and the most lucrative in the world. It works something like this: a fellow decides he is going to be a numbers operator, so he first picks out one of the public communications media capable of listing a different and completely unpredictable number every day. Usually it will be a certain combination of winning horses at a specified track. Thus, the second horse in the first race, the first horse in the third race, and the fifth horse in the fifth race at Hialeah might produce a winning number of 215. But the number can come from a wide variety of possible sources — dog races, the commodities exchange, or even a given combination of digits from the Dow-Jones industrial averages. Most numbers houses — even those within a syndicate — have their own distinct sources for winning numbers.

The next step is to find a sucker who is so enchanted by the 500 to 1 odds that he will give you anything from a nickle to a fin against the number of his choice coming out in the following day's paper. You multiply that sucker to infinity — shop girls, factory stiffs, sales clerks, bus boys, lawyers, welfare cases, school kids, storekeepers, clergymen, housewives, ditch diggers, accountants, cops, pimps, disc

47

jockeys, barbers, whores, and other pillars of the community — and you're in business. There are many variations, of course. Sometimes you offer less favorable odds for a better chance of winning — a payoff, say, for any combination of the three winning digits. Or you let the customers bet on individual digits and parlay them if they win. The numbers game is very flexible.

The most complicated part of the whole system is picking up your money. And that's where I came in. The lowest man in the hierarchy is called a runner. He picks up bets from his friends and from people around the neighborhood, makes a record of them, and turns the slips and the money over to a numbers drop — usually a neighborhood businessman who is also doing a little running on the side among his customers. As a bag man, I used to tote my little satchel around to certain drops every afternoon and pick up the day's take. At the same time, I also paid off any winners from the previous day.

Sometimes when I carried my bag back to Big Pastrami it would contain as much as $20,000 or $30,000. That is a lot of money, and when I first took the job I often toyed with the idea of carrying my bag elsewhere than to Big Pastrami. But, next to the law, dishonest bag men are about the only threat to an operator's profits, and he can be depended upon to take severe measures to discourage that sort of thinking. One bag man, who had the district next to mine for a while, was always talking about taking the boss's goodies and running off to Canada. He was warned a couple of times about the dangers of such talk, but he still kept on running his mouth about going to Canada. He finally made it. His body washed up on a beach outside Windsor.

My months as a bag man, I can honestly say, were among the most fruitful of my life. Not in terms of cash, you understand, because Big Pastrami had a mean habit of making payroll deductions to cover such contingencies as bail and hospitalization. It was his theory that when a bag man got himself pinched it was only because he had done something stupid, like running up to a cop with a pocketful of numbers and asking directions to the Griswold Building. And when he sent you into west-side territory for a bootleg pickup, it was your own inept behavior that allowed Delaney's boys to spot you and break a few arms and legs. So it was only right that we paid heavy insurance for our own keep, wasn't it?

No, it wasn't the keen business principles or the niceties of employee relations learned at the knee of Big Pastrami that made those days so memorable. Even though my pay was miserly and the working conditions would have made a union head-knocker break down and weep, my life was immeasurably enriched by the many new friends I made.

Typical of these was a woman named Alice. One of the most interesting illegal operations in Detroit at that time could be found in the back of a shabby little dress shop on Grand River. Not many customers went in for the shabby little dresses, but the bizarre merchandise offered as the principle line of trade attracted a regular clientele of surprising dimensions. This included everything from Blackbottom hod carriers and Corktown housewives to Grosse Pointe matrons and members of the city council. At various times, I saw professors from the University of Detroit, Ford Motor Company executives, and a former police commissioner modestly stealing away from this odd emporium. And modestly they should have stolen. One and all, they were tipping away with pockets and purses full of aphrodisiacs, blue movies, filthy photographs, and an astounding variety of mechanical devices designed to stimulate or appease the old twitch.

49

The store was owned and operated by Alice, a strikingly unusual woman if ever I met one. She was in her early 60's and might easily have passed for the president of the WCTU or a high-school English teacher. Nor was she entirely un-qualified for such positions — aside from her days as a pros-titute and a lady of the stage, she often spoke proudly of her early cultural period, when she attended Chautauquas and taught in a Sunday school. The years had dried her out some, but she was still a handsome woman, dignified, soft-spoken, bluish-white hair drawn severely back into a bun, tall and still graceful. She was the sort of fine looking woman that a fellow would have been proud to introduce as his mother, even though there was something distinctly un-motherly about her eyes. They were wide and dark and heavy lidded, and they seemed to brim with hints and sug-gestions and old fires well-banked against the years. There was a faint aura of the lascivious about her. Perhaps a hint of the tragic. She was too old for a young man — and she surely would have killed an old one.

As a sideline to her sideline, Alice also worked as a num-bers drop and that's how I got to know her. Even so, I must have made more than a dozen pickups before she decided to invite me into her clandestine sexual supermarket. And that was the durndest thing I ever did lay eyes on.

In sharp contrast to the dowdy, almost frumpy decrepi-tude of the dress shop proper, the salesroom in the rear had a strange, antique elegance about it. It was a large, dimly-lit room with glass display cases running around three sides. The walls behind the cases were honeycombed with slots and tantalizing little drawers of darkly stained oak. There were shelves holding rows of glass-stoppered laboratory bot-tles, round ones and square ones with brightly colored po-tions and powders and crystals showing through their frosty

50

sides. The fourth wall of the room was given over to a display of erotic paintings, some copied from the classics but altered in subtle and significant ways. And hanging from the ceiling in the middle of the room was a stuffed crocodile that had been rendered aggressively and improbably masculine by an imaginative taxidermist. The over-all effect was whorehouse-gothic, with elements of medieval alchemy and 19th century apothecary lending a solemn note of dignity.

The floor of this unlikely chamber was covered with an Oriental carpet of peculiar design. It was badly worn but obviously expensive, and Alice explained that it had once graced the salon of the most sumptuous bordello in San Francisco. In the dim light, I could see that the central figure of the design was a huge reptile similar in many respects to the crocodile that was hung above the floor. At first glance, the reptile in the rug seemed to be disporting himself in a field of golden flowers. Closer inspection proved these to be blossoms of flesh, golden-skinned courtesans submitting themselves to the embraces of many small but inhumanly proportioned reptiles identical to the one in the central design. And the things they were doing! Somehow I dropped my cigarette lighter, and bending to retrieve it I couldn't help but observe that in all those intricate groupings and couplings the pattern never once appeared to repeat itself. Alice assured me that this was so — no act of passion in all that broad tapestry was duplicated. Each grouping was unique, and there were nearly 500 of them. At least that's close to the number of times I dropped my lighter during subsequent visits.

I'm the first to admit that I wasn't an especially sophisticated youth, but I was certainly just as prurient as the next fellow, and Alice's shop provided a steady source of fresh amazements. Not least among these was Alice, herself. She

51

possessed a scholar's knowledge of her field, the sort of intimate acquaintance that comes only with years of study and devotion. She was the Bernard Lovell of the galaxies of erotica, and if you gave her the smallest encouragement she was capable of lecturing on the subject for hours at a time. Ever hungry for knowledge, I encouraged her.

"This," she would explain with all the aplomb of a garden club spinster, "is a gaudemiche, otherwise known as a dildoe. I think its function should be obvious to you."

And, blushing modestly, I would allow as how the function of the Lesbian gadget was, indeed, obvious.

She also trotted out for display a weird assortment of vibrating machines, shoehorn-looking things, condoms with fancy frills and ridges, contraceptive devices of every description, including diaphragms with erotic pictures painted on them and sterling silver IUD's, which always scared hell out of me because they looked as though they might come uncoiled at the wrong moment and give a fellow a nasty cut on the lip. The most wondrous of all these implements, to my young mind, was an item known as a merkin. Actually, the word designates two entirely different items, both quite improbable. In the most antique meaning, it is a phallic wig; and what, for the sweet love of love, anyone would ever want with one of those is more than I can say. But the merkins that Alice showed me were easily distinguished as being the sexual opposites of the dildoes.

Alice was quite discreet and never discussed her customers' individual quirks, but she did let drop the intelligence that both dildoes and merkins were very hot sellers among the good citizens of Detroit. This opened up interesting areas of speculation, and I couldn't help thinking what a ball they could have if all the owners of dildoes got together in Ford Auditorium with the devotees of the merkin.

They wouldn't even have to show up in person. They could simply summon a messenger service and send their imitation organs out to party it up by themselves. Just like a bunch of palolo worms hiding in the coral while their separable tails hold annual orgies on the surface of the lagoon.

I never knew anyone who admitted to owning a merkin. But I met a man in prison a few years later who knew what the thing was — and he was one of the few I ever met who did. Unfortunately, he was never able to give a comprehensible account of the source of his knowledge. He was totally insane, and the best he could get out was a babble that went like this:

"A ferkin of merkins, my good man. We'll peddle 'em in the pen and in the monkiaries to the celibate monks, to the bitter old men who do furious gymnastics with their hands. Left and right alternately for variety. Give 'em to the poor and give 'em to the sore, and disinherit your neighborhood whore."

Probably the weirdest thing in Alice's establishment was Hugo. He was a pop-eyed, fat little man without a feather on him. I mean, Jack, he was *bald*. No eyebrows, no eyelashes, no little threads sprouting from a nostril, no wild hairs on his earlobes. Nothing. Alice, who had known him for many years, claimed the deprivation was total from one end of him to the other, and that he had been that way ever since 1937, when he had acquired an exotic fungus from a Chinese merchant seaman.

Hugo made his living as a vendor of pornographic movies. He worked for Alice on a part-time basis as sort of a bootleg pharmacist. From his own sources, he would pick up drugs and herbs, then bring them around to the shop and mix them up into tasty aphrodisiacs for Alice's customers.

Some of Hugo's concoctions were pretty straightforward.

There was powdered rhinoceros horn, for instance, a gritty-looking substance that supposedly fetched up to $1,000 a pound in Hong Kong. Alice peddled the stuff for ten dollars an ounce, which led me to suspect either an unlikely degree of inflation in the Hong Kong market or an unscrupulous amount of adulterant in Hugo's horn. He had all the other traditional love potions, too: cantharides, hippomane — putrid stuff prepared from the vulval secretions of a mare — yohimbé, thorn apple, and much more similar junk that you'd have to be out of your mind to swallow. Hugo was a crude and uneducated little man, but you did have to give him credit for a good line of patter. He could talk quite learnedly about the solanaceae drugs, and the relative merits of black henbane and ground toads.

"Black hentbane," he would say, "is first class stuff. The same what did in Dristan and Isoldy. They was playin' checkers and they got so hooked up on the game they drunk this hentbane by mistake, see. And that gave 'em such a case of the hots they eventually get themselves offed. Guy wrote a play about it, if you don't believe me."

I believed him. To this day, I can't listen to Wagner without picturing Tristan and Isolde bent over a checkerboard with huge mugs of "hentbane" at their elbows.

Hugo's favorite aphrodisiac was powdered gekko lizard, and he was forever trying to get me to buy one of the damn things in the unpowdered state. That was so I would also have to buy a pepper mill to grind the ugly devil up, and a stack of recipes for brewing the finished potions. But I was too cunning for him. The trouble with lizard recipes, I had already learned from Alice, was that they always called for things like newt tails, jackal gall, eyes of newborn babes, and a lot of other stuff you have to shop around for just to give the lizard enough oomph.

54

I also happened to know that Hugo never used his own highly vaunted products, even though he had implicit faith in their efficacy. He even went so far as to shake out his trouser cuffs and wash his hands most thoroughly whenever he was through mixing up a batch of philtres. I asked him about this one afternoon.

"It's because of my wife," he said.

I already knew about his wife. She was a very large and very muscular Lesbian, known around Detroit's sapphic cocktail lounges as Gargantua. A most unlovely creature. She and Hugo shared a pure-white marriage of convenience. What she found in the union is more than I care to think about. But for Hugo, a just-by-the-skin-of-his-teeth latent homosexual, Gargantua was obviously either a weight-lifter image or a truck-driver substitute, as the psychologists might say. Which is to say, he wanted to be a faggot, but he was so frustrated and inhibited that he couldn't make the scene. So he didn't bed down with his wife — he just sat back and got his jollies from contemplating the pure horror of that unlikely happenstance.

"Yes," he explained, "it's my wife. Can you imagine what could happen if I tracked this stuff home with me and any of it got into her yogurt? Can you just imagine what that elephant might do to me in the throes of passion?"

"So what's your problem? You don't have to sleep with her, do you?"

"Ya bet your sweet ass I don't, baby. And that's just because I got enough sense not to take any of this merchandise home with me. Now, I got some new lizards here and I'll make you a special price on. . . ."

"Skip it," said I, picking up my numbers bag and heading for the door. "Alice already signed me up for holy orders. No more sex till I'm a full-fledged Trappist."

CHAPTER SIX

My job with Big Pastrami was rudely terminated when the law caught up with me on an old auto-theft charge and shipped me off to prison for my first dose of real time. This wasn't any 30-day rest cure in a county jail, this was one to five years for the Piper in the State Prison of Southern Michigan.

One prison sentence is the same as another, and all prisons are the same, no matter whether you are beaten regularly or simply slammed into a cell and forgotten. Because prison is a compound of immobility, feelings, and people. Those factors don't change with time or place. The present day convict who runs a jute mill under the auspices of a progressive penology is living in a world of bars identical to that of the Roman cutpurse who worked out his sentence in the emperor's lead mines. Regardless of conditions, prison is bad or incredibly bad according to the individual's capacity to suffer from it.

Some people kill themselves in prison. I've lost a number

of friends that way. Other people kill each other in prison. It's a brutal place; not so much because of the guards but because of the convicts themselves. Prisons become storage vaults for the unfeeling and fascist-minded animals of our world. Prisons concentrate these people into small, close areas. They distill the worst from society by their function and augment it by their nature.

But not everything about a prison is vicious. There are decent people who find their crooked ways in, there are harmless nuts and simple failures and off-beat characters of every description. Wrap them all up in the same cage and things begin to materialize that couldn't possibly find existence anyplace else.

The name of the cage is Waiting; months and years of waiting that have to be filled with something more than fights and knifings over cigarette debts and mincing pansies. With an abundance of idle time to kill, convicts spend many hours daydreaming of the good life and figuring out devious schemes for achieving eventual wealth. For the most part, these cell-hatched plans are not conspicuous either for intelligence or practicality. But many show evidence of considerable imagination.

One of the most imaginative fellows in Jackson prison was a man named Wimpy. He was slow talking and chubby, and he had a face that would have been easy to overlook if it hadn't somehow managed to radiate a superb confidence in the inevitability of success. I may be stupid, his little eyes seemed to say, but there are millions like me, and we will surely win. His sentence, I believe, was for something on the order of Conspiracy to Rob a Coin Box.

A great outlet for creative energies, and a dandy way to fill the empty hours, is the manufacture of spud juice. I have yet to hit a prison where you can't get a drink if you really put your mind to it. And in most joints the subject of alcohol amounts to a full-time preoccupation second only to Mom's apple pie — or something like that. In the recreation yard or in the chow line, the cons are always discussing various means of fulfilling the higher destiny of raisins, or how to make real, honest-to-god gin in your own toilet bowl.

The most common brew is made from potatoes or raisins, but almost anything will serve the purpose. My friend Wimpy used to set up batches of tomato purée in the plumbing crib where he worked in the maintenance department. He used to run it off in ten-gallon lots in an old water softener. The stuff went down like liquid leather, and it was absolutely guaranteed to petrify a man for 24 hours. It would also clean him out better than any laxative on the market. Wimpy's co-workers frequently came off their binges passing everything from blood to stomach lining.

My tastes in this respect were more demanding. While Wimpy was poisoning the inmate population with zeolitic ion exchange chemicals, I was setting up my own modest brews right in my cell. In my more antic moments, I occasionally turned out a crock of mead, using honey from the inmate commissary and yeast tablets from the dispensary. More often, though, I devoted myself to wine. I was able to make very passable wines from different flavors of jellies and jams, which were also available in the commissary. My Welches' Grape Jam Cell-Block-11 1957, for instance, was a delicate vintage that caressed your tongue like a ripe virgin and possessed a bouquet that would have brought new zest to the most jaded of palates. Unfortunately, the entire pressing ran to little more than one and a half quarts.

Friend Wimpy was a perfect study in marginal subsistance, a classic case of the socially submerged. In the course of a long and spotty career, he was never once known to pull off a caper without getting caught. And if he ever thought of anything sensible, he kept it pretty much to himself. A typical Wimpyism was his scheme to break out of prison through the sewer system. He carried it off, in his own direct manner, by constructing a makeshift aqualung from a length of five-inch drain pipe and jumping down a manhole. Even if he had had the wit to put a little compressed air in that pipe, his plan was doomed to failure. With his 90-pound scuba rig strapped to his back, he sank straight to the bottom and came within an inch of drowning — which is exactly what he would have done if a couple of onlookers hadn't dredged him out and helped to remove the tangle of tank and befouled clothing, a job that compared unfavorably with trying to peel the hide from a sick hippopotamus.

Wimpy's real masterpiece of bungling came to be known around the cell block as "The Case of the Great Stone Face," and even the hard-case guards used to break each other up yukking about it when word finally got out.

I was fortunate enough to witness most of this wild episode from its inception. It began on a Sunday afternoon when I was taking a short cut through the maintenance department on my way out to the handball courts. Sundays were always quiet in maintenance, with only one guard in the whole basement and not more than ten or 12 cons to handle emergencies. The guard was never very bright, since no one could sneak out of the joint through the basement, and the cons kept him well supplied with magazines, coffee, and sandwiches. So, naturally, Sunday afternoons in maintenance were a time to do a little illegal cooking of contraband food, or perhaps to set up a few gallons of spud juice and to take off the batch that had been set the week before.

59

I was just passing the carpenter shop when Wimpy reached out and hauled me in by the arm.

"How much water d'yuh put in plaster?" he demanded.

"I don't know," I told him. "I imagine it depends on what you want to use it for."

Looking past Wimpy's shoulder, I could see that we weren't alone in the shop. Another con, named Al Mc-Queen, was over in the corner slopping around in a bucket of plaster with a stick. The stuff was the consistency of skimmed milk.

"We're makin' a mold," said Wimpy. "Maybe you can help, huh?"

With that, he stuck his head out the door and checked the corridor in both directions. Then he closed the door and propped a two-by-four against it.

"What we're doin' is we're making a mold of Al's face. Then we fill that with mashed paper, see? An' all we got to worry about is makin' his hair. Won't nobody be able to tell the difference."

I saw what he was driving at, and it wasn't anything I cared to become involved in — not with a couple of shaky cats like those. Even mentioning a bed dummy in prison can get you permanent solitary for attempted escape.

"I'll tell you what, Wimpy. If I were silly enough to do anything like this, I think I'd want the plaster about the consistency of farina — not like the stuff we get on the main chow line, but like they serve the screws. Now, if you'll excuse me, I have a handball game waiting."

I turned toward the door, but Wimpy was already there.

"Come on," he said, "whyncha stick around till we get the stuff mixed at least?"

There is a certain etiquette in prison which demands that you don't withdraw your foot too abruptly once you've

60

stepped into something. The theory is that if a man stays around long enough to become at least a little bit involved no one will have to worry about him keeping his mouth shut, since even a fink isn't going to rat on himself. So I stood there and cursed myself for not having walked out before this jerk could tell me anything.

"Okay," I said. "Start mixing. I'll keep an ear on the corridor."

Wimpy dumped out most of Al's soupy mixture and poured in another half bag of plaster. That still wasn't enough, so he added half a bag of bolt anchor compound, a material used for patching concrete floors and fastening ironwork in walls. When this was mixed in, the stuff began to look stiff enough to work with.

I was more than a little nervous, and I kept as close to the door as I could. The next time I looked around Wimpy had Al stretched out on a bench and was smearing a generous handful of plaster across his forehead. I had never made any plaster casts before, but I could see where these guys might be heading for trouble. Al was a little man, hairier than a tarantula, and he had one of the heaviest beards in the prison. As of that moment, it looked as though he hadn't shaved for three or four days.

"Wimpy," I said, "don't you think you ought to shave him first?"

"Yeah, how's about keeping that gook outa my hair," said Al.

Wimpy slapped another handful of plaster across Al's mouth, cutting off any further protest from that end.

"What's the matter with you guys," he said indignantly. "You think I don't know what I'm doin'?"

"Okay," I said, "I'm leaving. But you better not cover up his nostrils. They'll have you for manslaughter."

61

The last I saw of Al as I slipped out the door was a shapeless blob of white, with a blue stubble still showing through where Wimpy hadn't yet gotten around to the second application.

After a good three hours on the handball court, the bugles that ended the recreation period were sounded, and I headed back through maintenance to my work assignment. Common sense told me to keep right on walking, but morbid curiosity won out and I ended up by taking the corridor past the carpenter shop. I just knew those idiots had done something terrible, committed some nameless horror of a blunder, and the thought of it had kept me off my game all afternoon.

I was right, too.

When I put my ear to the shop door I could hear a sharp metallic tapping on the other side. When I rapped on the door for entry, an eyeball showed itself at a crack, looked me over and let me in.

The eyeball was Jimmy from the tool crib. "Boy, am I glad to see you," he said. "Look what these stupid bastards have done!"

I looked over to where Al was still stretched out on the bench. His head was completely encased in plaster; 20 pounds of it, at least. There was a small, tightly rolled piece of paper protruding from the front of this shapeless blob — presumably this led to one of his nostrils, since his chest was still rising and falling. That seemed to be his only connection with the outside world, except for a small area over one ear where he had pawed away some of the plaster before it hardened.

Wimpy nodded sheepishly to me and Jimmy went back to work on Al's head with a hammer and cold chisel. It wasn't working very well — apparently because of the bolt anchor that had been mixed in — but he did have one chunk knocked loose at the side of the head. It had brought a large patch of hair with it.

Those poor, silly schnooks had tried to cast a one-piece mold of an entire head. Even if Al had been as hairless as an egg, it would have been impossible to remove that mess.

"It's just one Goddamn shame we're not outside," said Jimmy. "We could pour on a little more of this slop and dump the dumb son-of-a-bitch in a river."

This brought an angry snort through Al's one workable nostril.

"That chisel ain't doin' it," said Wimpy. "Whyn't we take that sledge over there and rap him right across the kisser?"

This suggestion only made Al flail about and kick the chisel out of Jimmy's hand. No one bothered picking it up because it was pretty apparent that Al was in there for keeps. And it was obvious that he couldn't stand any custodial counts in that condition.

At length, Jimmy and I prevailed upon Wimpy to turn Al in at the Infirmary. Al spent two weeks in there, and when he was released it was without his eyebrows or eyelashes. A lot of hair was also missing from his head, and he had lost most of his whiskers along with his skin. He was pretty upset about the whole thing, but he gave the guards such a good laugh at his predicament that no one even remembered to throw him and Wimpy into the hole.

Personally, I thought it was a very good sign that Wimpy had had the wit to try his scheme on someone else. It was probably the most intelligent thing he had done in years.

CHAPTER SEVEN

During that first stay in Jackson, there was a guard employed at the prison who made a lasting impression on me. His name was Titus Harrington, and I will not pretend that he was typical of the prison's custodial personnel — though he did have certain points in common with them. Harrington had been a prison guard for more than 35 years, and in the course of those years he had acquired as many quirks as the squirreliest old con in the joint. His most interesting peculiarity was his refusal to smoke anything but discarded cigarette butts. He smoked more than 100 of these every day just while he was on the job, not counting the collection he carried home in his pockets every night. But Harrington had pride, he did. He wouldn't bend his spine an inch to pick up the biggest butt in the cell block. And he wasn't a beggar, either. He simply let it be understood that if the ash tray on his desk weren't kept full of butts, his clerk could expect to retype all forms and requisitions a minimum of ten times.

Sometimes, to break the cloying monotony of it all, convicts play a little game called "Bugging the Cops." Its object is to make the screws doubt their own intelligence and competence — and if they come to doubt those things as much as the cons do, then it's a point for our side. A good example is the time some of the fellows decided to bug Harrington by giving him an extra inmate on his count.

Counts are a highly important, almost sacred part of prison life. They are taken a number of times each day, when the guards in the cell blocks and on the work assignments go around to check each individual convict to make certain none have escaped since the previous count. The guards list the prison numbers of the men who are missing and turn these in to the Main Office, where the Guard Captain checks them against the master count sheets. The men who are counted missing in their cells have to be counted present on their work assignments in order for the total to balance — and that has to be *exact*. One man too many or one man too few and the count must be rechecked. If it still doesn't jibe, the Deputy Warden is notified and all lesser custodial officials begin running in circles, getting ready to duck responsibility.

To create an extra man for Harrington's cell-block count, the men first assembled a number of props: a blanket, a sheet and pillow case, a foot locker, a handful of magazines, and a phony door card. This last item is a two-by-eight-inch strip of cardboard that slips into a slot on the cell door and identifies by name and number the man who is supposed to be locked in the cell. The most important thing in their collection was a duplicate cell key made from a putty impression that Harrington's clerk had taken of the original while Harrington was sleeping at his desk.

With everything in readiness, the men waited until just

65

before the 6:00 P.M. count, then went up to an unoccupied cell on the fourth tier, way at the top of the cell block, and opened it with the duplicate key. It took them less than a minute and a half to slide the footlocker into the cell, make up the bed, and scatter the magazines around to give the place a lived-in look. They put the dummy card in the door, turned the cell light on, and beat it back to their own cells in time for the count.

Harrington was never too swift when it came to taking count, and when he came to the gimmicked cell it stopped him cold. It didn't look right to him, but it frequently happens that a man gets moved into a cell without the block officer knowing about it, so Harrington licked his pencil and carefully entered the phony number on his count sheet as a missing man. He looked the cell over one last time, then finished his count, and sent it up to the Main Office.

Fifteen minutes later the Office turned up the discrepancy. Harrington not only showed a man missing where there shouldn't have been a man at all, he showed one who was supposed to have been paroled two weeks previously.

Harrington spilled cigarette butts all over the stairs getting up to fourth to check that cell again. Sure enough, the name card was still on the door and someplace there had to be a convict to match it. Harrington copied the number down three times to make certain he had it right. Then he ran for the Main Office, ready to do battle for the integrity of his count.

As soon as he was gone, the boys went up to fourth and stripped the cell clean. The door was relocked, the foot locker was given back to its owner, and the door card was flushed down a toilet. By the time Harrington came back to make another mad scramble up to fourth — this time with the Captain and two lieutenants hot on his heels — that cell was just as barren and empty as any other unused cell in the prison.

The brass practically had to put restraining straps on old Harrington to get him out of the block and quiet him down.

The most expert bugger in the prison was a man in his middle 50's named Haskel Harris, possessor of a rare but wasted genius. Haskel was a college man, a graduate of Yale, with a keen wit and a highly developed taste for alcohol. On the street, he made his living as a bum, though not in any sense of the word as an ordinary bum. Haskel specialized in unusual approaches designed to startle potential benefactors into coming across generously for his alcohol fund. Approaching a gentleman coming out of the Sheraton Cadillac, he might say something like, "Pardon me, mister, kin ya spare a quarter so's I kin get myself wormed?" Or maybe, "I still owe two bits on my last circumcision." For female clients, he usually tried to inject a subtle hint of family tragedy to play on their sympathy. "Your pardon, ma'am," he would say. "I hate to trouble you for anything so trifling as a dime, but my mother needs an abortion."

Haskel worked in the prison textile mill, a long brick building filled with looms that turned out fabric to make sheets and garments for the numerous inmates of Michigan's prisons and hospitals. The air in this place was thick with lint. Walls and floors vibrated unpleasantly to the roar of the looms and the rhythmic slap-a-dap of shuttles. It was not a nice place to work. There was a sharp sense of futility about the whole operation — a man worked at his loom to make cloth to make denim trousers so he would have something to wear when he left the cell block to go to the mill to make cloth to make denim trousers . . . . slap-a-dap, slap-a-dap, slap-a-dap.

Twenty-five feet from the building, and parallel to it, was one of the main prison walls, a towering, unscalable 40 feet of smooth concrete, with guard towers spaced along the top. The authorities were sensitive about that wall because the mill was so close to it. They worried that someone might tie a rope to the roof of the mill and swing himself over the wall. They fretted over the possibility that someone might even slide a plank out to the top of the wall from one of the mill windows. They were just awfully touchy about that wall.

One afternoon, while his loom was temporarily shut down, Haskel fell to contemplating the wall. In due course, inspiration came to him and he motioned a couple of friends to follow him to the basement, an immense catacomb running the length of the building and stuffed to the gills with cotton bales and rolls of cloth.

Haskel and his friends let themselves out a basement door and sneaked around behind the powerhouse, where they secured a couple of buckets, a pick, three shovels, and a push broom. From a con who worked around the coal pile, they also acquired an extension cord. Haskel filled the buckets with ordinary dirt, then the three of them carried their booty back to the basement of the mill. The rest of the afternoon was spent making more trips outside with the buckets to haul in more dirt.

By quitting time, Haskel had accumulated a large and untidy pile of dirt that was only made more conspicuous by a partially concealing layer of rags. The pick, buckets, shovels, and extension cord were hidden in a pile of bales. The broom was propped openly against a wall, and a nearby toilet was clogged to overflowing with a cubic foot of rich dirt. Satisfied with their work, Haskel and his friends sneaked back upstairs in time to leave the mill along with the rest of the cons who were returning to their cell blocks for the night.

No cons went to work in the mill the next day. During the night, an eagle-eyed guard had detected the unmistakable signs of tunnel work. The Warden, the Deputy, and all the top brass inspected the evidence and saw the obvious: a group of malcontents were digging a tunnel from the basement of the textile factory to that wall, only 25 feet away. Hidden someplace in that basement there was the entrance to a tunnel. Everybody *knew* there was a tunnel there.

So, for an entire week the looms were deliciously silent while crews of prison guards moved aside endless stacks of 600-pound cloth bolts, cursed the immobility of huge cotton bales, and crawled through the lint on their hands and knees, tapping the floor for signs of a tunnel.

In contrast to such sane and wholesome outlets as these, the official big gig offered by the authorities in their modern penology bag is Group Therapy. Spell that in capitals and color it sacred.

For me there was never any escape from group therapy, since I was always quite candid in admitting that I was a thief because I enjoyed the stimulation of crime and because I had a marked aversion to the 40-hour week. This didn't go over at all well in a system geared to the premise that a thief is never a thief through preference, but through the workings of a warped id. Nature's abhorence of a vacuum, I tell you, is as nothing compared to the psychologist's loathing of a simple and direct explanation.

So I was always getting roped into these sordid little get-togethers where seven or eight of us were supposed to sit down with a bug doctor and twitch in merry unison. The drill at these things is to cop out, ever so hesitantly, that you

69

aren't completely at ease with the idea of being castrated, or that you don't feel happy in a penitentiary environment. Then the therapist asks for a show of hands from everyone similarly afflicted, and you are supposed to feel just awfully relieved to learn that you are not alone in your aberration. A marvelous system. I could go in there twice a week and have my maladjustment reaffirmed.

The whole scene is a very sticky go, because you are caught in a situation where you can't win. On the one hand, there is the assumption that you have to be at least a short distance around the bend or you wouldn't be in prison in the first place. On the other hand, there is the fact that if anyone in a prison tries to behave sanely and rationally, as he might in a normal environment, he is immediately marked as an eccentric. Prisons are another world, with a continuum of space and time quite unrelated to the one beyond the walls. Right and wrong take on new meanings. Goals become foreshortened to the ends encompassed by length of sentence and parole eligibility. And certain words become very important. People in prison — inmates and officials alike — tend to exert themselves tremendously to achieve such improbable ends as *adjustment, rehabilitation,* and *release.* Eventually, those words achieve a significance entirely divorced from the reality of any space or time — and their pursuit, in an ordinary frame of mind, is about as fruitful as trying to win at roulette through telekinesis. One year of this Kafkaesque double-think, and a sane man is ready to resign from the human race and spend his remaining days in a rose bush counting aphids.

So you wind up twisting yourself into a neurotic pretzel to adapt yourself to the world of prison, and you do what you can to make the best of it. You pretend that you are learning a new sense of responsibility and finding great satis-

70

faction in a work assignment that is completely unrewarding and in which you cannot really feel involved — the pointless shuffling of papers to move other convicts from one cell to another, working to maintain the antiquated plumbing and wiring of the prison that is separating you from life, making uniforms for prison guards, or stamping out license plates. You pretend to be one of the boys and you pretend to conform to their silly "convict code" — a list of solid-brother "thou shalt nots" that is never observed in practice but stoutly defended by even the worst stool pigeons in the penitentiary.

And, if you are the eager type, you can twist yourself into even fancier curves in those group therapy sessions. I used to get quite a chuckle watching the contortions of the guys who thought they could con the psychologists into recommending them for special parole consideration. Man, the phony, transparent frauds they put down. One guy used to show up every week with a new insight into his personality — "It was them cookies my ma wouldn't give me when I was four years old. All my life I been kicking in these stores 'cause I got 'em confused with cookie jars." Or, "Sure, she told me she was eight years old. But I misunderstood her — I thought she said she was ten."

I suppose there may have been some benefit to it. If a man came up with enough stories, he might ultimately hit upon one that really had some significance. But it never worked for me.

There was one man in our therapy group who had managed to hold on to his individuality without having all the rebellion rooted out of his soul — though he seldom attended the sessions due to the amount of time he spent in solitary confinement. We called him Mazz. And Mazz had

71

his own way of rebelling. Where others were quietly sullen and evasive when it came to obeying petty regulations, Mazz openly flouted them. What's more, he did it with flair. No matter what he was protesting, he had a splendid sense of the *beau geste,* and it wasn't lost on the other cons.

One of the finest of his noble gestures was the Great Bean Protest. This came about shortly after the prison hired a new steward, a former guard who was barely competent to run off a batch of boiled laundry. You might say he didn't know from beans, because the first time he prepared them they were scarcely cooked. I was sitting with Mazz when this particular mess was served, and I could see a protest building up as he angrily mashed his fork into the beans. They were very hard and extremely small, swimming in a sauce mostly composed of the water in which they had been parboiled. They looked about as palatable as a dish of roach powder.

"Say," Mazz yelled, standing up from the table, "summon the bastard responsible for these beans."

A ghastly hush fell over the mess hall. Mazz hadn't exactly accused them of putting salt in the coffee, but any sort of disturbance in the mess hall can easily blossom into a riot with steel trays sailing in all directions and a heavier concentration of food in the air than on the tables.

The guards began heading for Mazz, and the steward stuck his head out of the kitchen.

"You!" Mazz said, holding up a fistful of the offending beans. "Dumb son-of-a-bitch. Don't you even know how to cook a Goddamn bean?"

That's as far as Mazz got before they hauled him off to solitary confinement. He still had the beans in his fist as they led him away, and he was still muttering obscenely about the "idiot cook."

72

Two weeks later, Mazz came out of the hole. They let him out at noon in time for the meal, and the Captain himself escorted Mazz to the mess hall. They were serving beans again. The Steward was on hand also with a look of welcoming forgiveness on his face. And he personally served Mazz a double ration of beans.

"There you are, my boy," he said. "You look like you're pretty hungry."

Mazz looked hungry, alright. He was bearded and gaunt after his two weeks on bread, water, and potatoes. He also looked disgusted as he ran his fork through the beans, then thoughtfully picked one up and bounced it on the floor.

"Ignorant son-of-a-bitch!" he screamed. "Ain't you learned in two weeks how to cook a Goddamn bean yet?"

That time they gave him an entire month in the hole. But, by way of proving him right and giving him incentive for further demonstrations, they also made the Steward learn how to cook beans.

Mazz was extreme in his reaction to authority. In one way or another, though, everyone reacts in an extreme way to the regimentation of prison. They turn into vegetables, or they hold themselves tightly in, or they blow off at seemingly insignificant provocations. Prison is a totally unnatural world. It's a million miles and a million years from everything that is good and comprehensible in life. It's fear and loneliness. It's wanting something simple, like a Coney Island hot dog, until there is nothing in the world but that one thing. It's a man wanting to cry because he suddenly realizes that he hasn't heard a child's voice for more than ten years. And a woman. God, but how you can hunger for the softness and the warmth and the love of a woman. You ache for the solace of soft arms and tender words. You learn the agony of not being able to give pleasure to a woman of your

73

own, of not being able to seek out the strings that will set her whole body to vibrating with your own, not hearing the sudden huskiness in her voice, or seeing your own ecstasy in her half-closed eyes. You die for all the places you cannot put your lips, all the warm corners you cannot burn with your tongue. And you want to *give* to a woman until you can't stand it. But not just to any woman. You want *the* woman. The one who is right and who will make up for all those empty years.

The needing, though, can sometimes weigh too heavily. Those old jokes about talking-to-yourself-is-okay-but-watch-it-when-you-begin-answering-back are not so funny around a prison. I mean, like, I've talked to myself many times in the emptiness of a cell. Had some pretty good conversations, in fact. But I never got terribly radical about it. Some fellows go pretty deep into that bag over a period of years. Sometimes it's a temporary and a harmless thing that helps a man through a very rough time. Other times it's a doorway to insanity. It can go either way, but there's nothing unusual about solitary mutterings in the cell blocks at Jackson.

In the cell below mine there was an old man named Clancy who had gone quietly and harmlessly insane during his tenth year of confinement. He didn't bother anyone, and neither the convicts nor the guards ever interfered with his delusions. When they let us out into the yard for recreation, Clancy always wandered off by himself, carrying on his endless conversation with God knows who. If any of us had occasion to speak to him in the yard, thus interrupting his dialogue, it was considered a breach of etiquette not to acknowledge his imaginary friend.

"Hiya, Clancy," we'd say. "You, too, pal," nodding to-

74

ward whatever volume of empty air Clancy was currently addressing.

And Clancy would grin and nod and shuffle his feet with delight. It was such a small thing, to humor the old man's fantasy. One of the few good things of prison was the uniformity of kindness offered to him even by the creeps who normally found delight in torment. Not that it would have been especially healthy for them to offer anything else. Touched by the gods, was Clancy. Or maybe only by Mercury, the good god of thieves and dogs.

When he was in his cell, Clancy was in touch with all the world. While the rest of us were listening to constipated disc jockeys and high-school basketball games, Clancy was receiving secret instructions from Interpol over his earphones. None of the rest of us could get that particular station, but that was only because we didn't know how to position our cots just so, kitty-corner across our cells, to cut out the small interference generated by the three authorized radio channels. Clancy was doing some sort of undercover work for Interpol. He didn't make any particular secret of his police duties, however. About twice a day he'd collar someone in the cell block and inform him that he had uncovered some very compromising information and was going to have to file a report on it that evening. It was much to the credit of the cons in that prison that such talk never got the old man killed.

At times, alone in his cell, the old man would come a little bit unwound and give in to spells of hypochondria. Usually the only way we could tell he was having one of his spells was when one of us spotted him crouching at the back of his cell eating APC tablets like salted peanuts. Then two or three of us would have to stand around in front of his cell talking about Interpol or inventing an imaginary person

to catch his interest and pull his mind back from his intes-
tines. Sometimes, though, he would begin calling out after
everyone was locked up for the night, complaining that his
pure white hair was turning brown or that his eyeball was
loose. His favorite complaint centered on the teeth he no
longer had.

"Hey, fellers," he'd yell. "Me teeth are fallin' out!"

And someone always jollied him: "Get some new ad-
hesive, Clancy." Or: "Put 'em under your pillow, Clancy.
When you wake up in the morning you'll find the good
fairy."

Pretty soon guys would be laughing, and we'd hear
Clancy's cackle drifting up from below. Then we'd hear him
positioning his cot just so and taking down his earphones
to make his report to Interpol, and we'd know Clancy was
alright again.

CHAPTER EIGHT

When I came out of prison that first time I jumped right straight into a new hustle. I wanted nothing more to do with organized crime, or with established cliques of hoodlums. Every time you fall in with a crew like that you wind up taking orders from some know-nothing torpedo-type. Moreover, you don't get to meet so many new and interesting people as when you are a non-affiliated thief.

So I became a crowd hustler. I took to making the circuit with the fellows who specialized in boosting loose goodies from people in public places — theaters, restaurants, parades, sporting events, picnics, anyplace where there was likely to be a high concentration of humanity and valuables. It's a hustle that was old when toga-clad thieves were heisting chariot whips and stray denarii from careless Romans at the Colosseum. And if there isn't much traffic in chariot whips today, there is still a hot demand for cash. Which is not to mention portable radios, cameras, fur coats, and all the other things that people carry around with them.

Contrary to popular opinion, very little of this loot comes from race-track patrons. The association of thieves and ponies is largely a myth nurtured by the late Damon Runyon. What with track dicks, city cops, racing commissioners, state police, and other law-enforcing oddments, it's almost worth your parole to go near a horse. Crowd hustlers tend to shy away from anything that has legal betting attached to it. They concentrate on the big, popular sports such as baseball, football, hockey, and basketball, though not to the exclusion of participant sports such as bowling, golf, or even tennis.

It's the focus of attention that gives a crowd hustler his biggest edge. People at a game aren't thinking about being robbed in the first place. And once the game is moving, they don't see anything but the players. The same holds true for the theater. If a playgoer is wrapped up in Beckett or Albee or Ionesco, he is effectively numb to financial deprivation. Sometimes, when the action is especially good, even the hustlers forget what they're doing. One time I saw a dip put his hand in a mark's pocket and then forget all about it, while they both stood frozen in criminal intimacy watching a Norwegian skier named Ansten Samuelstuen make a record jump of 316 feet at Steamboat Springs.

My own favored areas of operation were aquatic events, tennis matches, and sports car races. Long ago, I came to the obvious conclusion that my success as a thief was going to depend heavily on the affluence of my clients, and I discovered that the sportier sports seemed to bring out a better-heeled set of spectators. The merchandise was not only in greater quantity and of superior quality but was treated in a more cavalier manner by its owners. Sports-car rallies offered one significant advantage. If I had a bad day with the spectators, I could turn my attention to the contents of their cars, mostly easy-to-enter convertibles. And if that still didn't net me enough to get home on, I wasn't above clouting a whole car. That sort of thing is riskier than snatching an untended transistor TV set, but at least you have something to show for your work. This is to larceny what job insurance is to honesty.

I've always had a special affection for the old-timers in the rackets, partly because the ones who are still around mark the end of an era in crime that will never be seen again, and partly because of the inner qualities that kept them going in their chosen professions instead of finding nice, soft niches in life as janitors, night watchmen, and child molesters. Crime, at best, provides a precarious existence for its practitioners, and the colorful relics who stick with it to the end are invariably men of a special cut.

The best crowd hustler in the business, for instance, was a guy named Heini Klein. He was already in his 70's when I met him, but he was still the slickest thief ever to come down the bleachers. Heini used to hustle in the old country before he came over here around the turn of the century, and what he didn't know about taking a mark would never get you arrested.

Heini had a motto. He quoted it frequently and adhered to it religiously: "A good thief should look like an honest victim." That's exactly how Heini looked — a little shadow of a man, plain as a cell block wall, with a touch of arthritis and such an unmitigated look of innocence that strangers felt like kicking him for his apparent simpleness. Sometimes he affected a Malacca cane that he swore he had clouted from Otto von Bismarck at a yacht race on the Starnberger See. If that really was Bismarck's cane, the old boy probably *gave* it to Heini. There was something about Heini that would have inspired trust in the flinty heart of a pawn-

79

broker. He was such a mild and kindly looking old gentle-man that when people had to go to the john after the seventh inning they'd ask him to watch their kids. Many of his best scores came from people asking him to hold their seats and keep an eye on their things. Heini kept an eye on them alrighty — all the way to the nearest fence.

Heini's specialties were cameras and binoculars. He'd move in on his mark as polite and old-worldly as you please, and before you knew it he'd be squinting out at the field through a borrowed pair of Bausch & Lombs, or exclaiming naively over a $500 Leica. And the first time a player made a 50-yard run, or slammed out a homer, Heini simply evap-orated into the crowd.

In recent years, Heini has been forced to dissipate his genius on more sedentary gaffs — pigeon drops, bar hustles, short cons — out of consideration for his health. Even the best hustler has to cut and run at times, and a thief with arthritis just doesn't have much advancement potential.

Heini would have been a great disappointment to those who expect their lawbreakers to come with shifty eyes, five o'clock shadows, and prison pallors. Most thieves, in fact, look pretty ordinary, and if you hustle outdoors at golf courses and such places you can cultivate a better than av-erage suntan. The only crowd hustler I knew who really conformed to the Lombrosian ideal was a little creep affec-tionately known to the light-fingered clan as "the Creep." He had a face like an armpit and a personality that only a warden could love. Cops used to dog his heels like flies after a garbage scow. The only time he didn't get arrested for what he was pulling was when he was scalping tickets for the hockey games at Olympia Stadium — and then the squares were talking his prices down until he was getting less for the tickets than what he'd originally paid. We were always glad to have this guy around because he took the heat off the rest of us.

I took great pains to avoid looking like a hood. If that meant a raglan sweater and tapered slacks at a National Open, then that's what I wore while casing the gallery or shaking down the locker room. If it also meant an occasional pair of Bermuda shorts — well, that was just one of the sacrifices demanded by any profession.

I learned a great deal from Heini, but the one thing he was never able to get across to me was how to pick a pocket. Picking pockets is an art for which I never had the least bit of talent. It demands a certain steady-handed delicacy that always seemed to escape me, and the few attempts I made generally resulted in unpleasant little scenes that cost everyone a sorry price in dignity — people yelling "Cutpurse!" and "Stop, thief!" like something out of Dickens. Disgraceful. And what happened to me the last time I tried picking a pocket shouldn't happen to a stool pigeon.

Working a hockey game at Olympia, I spotted a mark carrying his wallet in the pocket of a topcoat slung over his shoulder. This makes for a very soft touch. I got hold of the wallet with no trouble at all. A real cinch. I was just easing it out of the pocket, practically counting the money, when I became aware of a very unsettling thing. Someone had his hand in my hip pocket clear up to his elbow! I spun around so fast that I peeled my mark right out of his seat, but by the time I got untangled from him and the topcoat, I'd already been made for my wallet. This was very humiliating, and when I finally found enough nerve to tell Heini about it he told me I would probably be better off in another line of work. I agreed.

It takes more than just basic dishonesty to make a good pickpocket. It takes a special type of person, a combination

81

of magician, psychologist, contortionist, and white rabbit. Just such a combination was Sammy Sloane, who was the best dip in Detroit. Guys who wanted to pose as cops to shakedown some sucker used to hire Sammy to lift wallets and identification from legitimate cops. He could steal anything from anyone. His favorite hustle was snatching wristwatches right off people's wrists.

Sammy's sense of humor was a rare and spontaneous thing that gave birth to the wackiest situations in the weirdest places. He used to get on buses and, just for the hell of it, pick two strangers and switch their wallets around. Wherever Sammy went around Detroit, he left behind him a scattering of confused and thoroughly disoriented people.

One time after he had just made a report to his parole officer on the sixth floor of the Cadillac Square Building, he got into a self-service elevator with two female probation officers who worked on the same floor. They didn't know he was a parolee, and as the elevator descended they discussed between themselves the tribulations of their profession. Sammy listened with growing disgust as they twittered on about the low moral character of criminal offenders, the laxity of the courts in sentencing felons, and the lamentable coddling of prisoners in the penitentiaries. Then, just before the elevator reached the ground floor, the power went off.

The two ladies lapsed into immediate silence, and Sammy could hear them shrinking into opposite corners of the blacked-out compartment. Suddenly, he was smitten with one of his inspirations. He began holding a whispered monologue with himself: "Really, now, you mustn't . . . . please try to control yourself, Miss. . . . Well, if you. . . . Oh, that's very nice . . . . ," all the while making kissing noises on the back of his hand, shuffling his feet, thumping the wall, working his zipper, and creating other suitable sound effects.

When the lights came back on a few minutes later, and the elevator resumed its descent, the two probation ladies were still cowering in their own corners and Sammy in his — with his collar awry, his coat unbuttoned, and his breath coming in ragged gasps. As the elevator doors opened, he turned to his two startled companions, tipped his hat, and said with the most suggestive leer he could muster:

"To which of you charming ladies am I indebted for the most delightful ride of my life?"

Then he left the elevator, leaving the two ladies of the Court glaring suspiciously at one another.

That episode is typical of the way a pickpocket's mind works. Dips have always been noted for innovation, for the mental and physical agility that allows them to survive in a very risky and demanding business. Almost without exception, they are well above average in the essential human quality of cunning. It was the ingenuity of pickpockets, for instance, that gave us our word "racket," indicating an organized swindle. The evolution from the original sense of the word, meaning a loud and disturbing noise, began with the diversionary tactics of pickpockets in the 17th and 18th centuries. A common practice among the boys back in those days was to set off a string of firecrackers, or to goose some old broad in a public place, or otherwise to create a disturbance that would draw a large crowd, where pockets could be picked more conveniently.

This approach has evolved into such modern ploys as the fake fight, the double jostle, and the sign gimmick. The bit with the sign has come to be very common. A dip will station himself in a department store next to one of those signs that says BEWARE OF PICKPOCKETS. When people come by

83

and look at the sign they automatically check whatever pocket their money is in. They might as well walk over and hand it to the dip. The device works so well, in fact, that Sammy used to carry the signs around with him and hang them up wherever he happened to be working.

Sammy had one weakness that was not at all typical of the skilled and narrowly specialized class of criminals who pick pockets. He had an absolute passion for snatching purses.

I don't know what possible inducement there could be for a fellow to get into such a screwy line of work; not when there are so many opportunities to develop his talents in more forthright businesses such as burglary or armed robbery. But snatchers far outnumber dips, and most of them seem quite content with their occupation, only feeling occasional twinges of regret when they find themselves trapped in the back of an elevator with a hot purse under their coat and a gaggle of bargain-talking females between them and the door.

During my years around Detroit, I came to know a great many men who made their living this way — an assortment of characters straight out of *The Beggar's Opera*. Some of them were quite decent fellows and, even though they were eminently dishonest, they stuck to a code of ethics that demanded equal consideration for the victim *and* the cash.

Unfortunately, just as with many another once-honored trade, the traditional art of the cutpurse has fallen upon evil times. The profession is overrun with amateurs, heavy-handed louts of small talent and even smaller character who would be better employed on a rock pile. Purse snatching has become the catchall of crime. It's a last resort for down-at-the-heels burglars, unemployed stick-up artists, and others who have lost the professional drive and are too lazy to go straight. It's a lark for juvenile delinquents, a source of small revenue for welfare bums, a spur-of-the-moment thing for drunks — and to many it's an outlet for something dark and vicious inside of them.

One of the last of the old-time professional snatchers still around is a guy named Chauncy. He is a little butterball of a man with gray hair, rheumy eyes, and the homeliest face this side of a basset hound. He is a sweet and gentlemanly fellow, and he often goes far out of his way to avoid hurting his victims. There is never any rough stuff when Chauncy is on the job. No dislocated arms or broken jaws. No switch-blades or tire chains or other cute weapons from the arsenal of the hoodlum. Chauncy is as soft in heart as he is in belly. He is also something of a poet, in his own larcenous fashion.

"My friend," he used to tell me, "women are flowers. They are rare blossoms that must be treated with kindness and respect. When you remove their nectar you must do it gently. With love, as it were."

Chauncy pulled his first job way back in 1902. Rather inauspiciously, he began by stealing a car. He didn't know how to start the thing, much less how to drive it, so he fell back on the obvious expedient of hauling it away with a horse. As Chauncy told it, that car heist was the crime of the century — and well it might have been. The old heap he took was the only automobile for 200 miles around, and until he abandoned his loot to a posse, Chauncy was certainly the most sought-after car thief in those parts.

When I met him, he had been clouting purses for more than 40 years, and if he had never learned anything more about stealing cars, he had certainly learned everything there was to know about purses. Seeing Chauncy in action was a rare and wonderful thing. He probably did more for the science of buzzing a moll than Dillinger ever thought of doing for the art of busting a jug.

Chauncy was a true originator. His most famous gambit, known as "the Flying Chauncy," was simple and direct. He would first spot a likely victim on an open and fairly deserted stretch of sidewalk. Then he would begin running toward her, full tilt. Not directly into her, mind you, but at a tangent so close that it looked as though he were going someplace beyond. There would be a peculiar, unfocused look about his eyes which resulted from trying to stare off into the distance without losing sight of the purse.

"Hey, there!" he'd yell, arm outstretched and index finger cocked up in a halting gesture. "Hey, wait for me!"

You could almost see a commuter special pulling away 50 feet ahead of him.

Invariably, the victim would freeze in her tracks, not having the least idea which way to dodge. Her head would swivel back and forth a couple of times, first toward the pudgy ball of energy bearing down on her, then toward the nonexistent train.

Never breaking stride, and with beautiful precision, Chauncy would dart out a practiced hand for the purse and head for the next corner, where he could catch a real streetcar.

The system had obvious advantages — a running start, and a victim who was standing conveniently still. And she was usually too startled at the sudden loss to put up an immediate stink. Chauncy picked his shots and never missed a purse. Nor was he ever known to knock a woman flat, or even so much as to ruffle her permanent wave with the slip stream of his passage. But it was a subtle system, and not everyone could handle it.

One time Chauncy was trying to teach the rudiments of

86

the profession to the Creep, previously mentioned in these pages. Chauncy regarded the Creep as a charity case, or a kind of job rehabilitation project. Time and again, when the Creep came waltzing up to him with a purse tucked blithely beneath his arm, Chauncy would patiently explain, "No, no, you clod! Out in the open like that will only get you pinched for soliciting."

The Creep finally put himself out of business one day when he tried a Flying Chauncy on a woman at a bus stop. The Creep went barreling past his victim with a head of steam that would have made Chauncy proud. He had the proper focus to his eyes, the index finger was cocked at the proper angle, everything was perfect. Except for the mailbox. The owner of the purse was standing right beside one, and when he snatched the purse in mid-flight, the strap caught on the handle of the letter slot. It was a tough strap, and the purse stopped abruptly — while the Creep kept going in a horizontal pratfall along 30 feet of sidewalk — until he fetched up against a lamp post.

Many of the same techniques used by pickpockets are also used by purse snatchers. Some are even more effective with women than with men, since women tend to be less suspicious or, at least, they are apt to suspect the wrong thing. A common tactic, for instance, is to bump into your victim by way of distraction while removing the money. As often as not, when you bump into a man he immediately reaches for his wallet. But when you bump into a woman she glares at you.

"My boy," Chauncy once told me, "I've collected glares in my time that would have paralyzed a boa constrictor. I've also had reactions considerably more violent. I recall one time I had a fine target all lined-up in a department store, a matronly woman who had just made a couple of purchases

87

and had flashed a roll of bills big enough to choke a mint. So I bumped into her sort of casual-like and sliced the purse with a Gillette blade, one of those new stainless steel jobs. Can't beat 'em for cutting purses; even those tough nylon jobs they're making nowadays. You can slice away for weeks at a time without having to change blades. Well, anyway, I sliced the old girl's purse and I managed it very skillfully, if I do say so myself. But before I could extract the roll, she turned on me like something out of a Greek tragedy. 'Masher! Unhand me!' she says. Shrieked was more like it, and so help me those were her very words. Masher. And before I could explain that I was nothin' but a purse snatcher, she belted me right in the face with the purse.

"It was terrible, I tell you. Keys, money, cosmetics, and a regular blizzard of green stamps went flyin' all over the place. With her yelpin' all the time about her Goddamn virtue. I went all my life without getting called anything like a masher. She could have gotten me pinched on a sex rap. At my age!"

When Chauncy became too short in the wind for his famous flying tactics, he was forced to fall back on more subtle techniques that demanded less agility. But he didn't give up willingly. He switched only after a couple of grayhaired little old ladies chased him all around Cadillac Square one day and ran him half to death. After that, he found it much easier hustling downtown elevators during the rush hours. This is a technique known as "hanger binding," and it requires a great deal of finesse. The idea is to spot a purse on a shoulder strap, open it or slit it, and remove the money without causing any uproar. It's a very popular hustle in metropolitan areas. So popular, Chauncy told me in disgust, that he once found himself in an elevator with four other people — and two of them were in the same business he was.

I still find myself endlessly fascinated by the old-timers, like Heini and Chauncy, who are still around after everyone else has left the party. They serve as a reminder of how things were before most of the professionalism went out of crime. And they give crime a sense of continuity that is much warmer and far more human than the only other permanent fixture in my world — the cell that is always waiting to end it.

The old-timers also have some of the damnedest stories to tell. On my way through Los Angeles one time I was invited to the home of a friend — an ex-Teamsters official out of Detroit — for an evening of stud poker. It was a friendly type of game that ended up running for two days straight. Poker is not my game, and 48 hours at a whack is not my style. But one of the men sitting in on the game was Nick the Greek, and the chance to meet and talk with him was worth the ordeal.

This was only a couple of years before he tapped out for the last time. He was a pretty faded Greek in those days, though still witty and hawk-like and sharp with the cards. The big days were all gone for Nick. Now he was living out on Wilshire Boulevard somewhere, sitting in on games with small timers like me, and finding just as much pleasure in our five-dollar limit as when he dropped $605,000 to Arnold Rothstein in the biggest stud poker pot ever recorded. In those days Nick was a giant. Gangsters, politicians, show girls, college professors; everybody knew Nick and everybody liked him. He played poker with Grover Whalen, had dinner with the Duke of Windsor, and traded jokes with Dutch Schultz. Sharing a green-topped table with Nick the Greek was sharing something gone forever. It was Texas

Guinan, Legs Diamond, the Ziegfeld Follies — a whole period of American history drawn into one poker hand.

All the time we were playing, I kept hoping Nick would tell about one of his famous bets — the time he staked $500,000 in poker winnings on the turn of a single card, the time he dropped $280,000 to Laughing Joe Titus on one roll of the dice, or maybe the time he lost $300,000 at bridge, a game he barely knew. Instead, he fell to chuckling over a ten-dollar bet he'd lost in 1930.

"Darnedest thing I ever got into," he said. "I walked into a speak on 42nd Street one afternoon. There was just one other guy in there, so I sat down with him and ordered a drink. Pretty soon we got to talking about gambling, which was alright with me, naturally, because I am a gambler, and this guy suggests that we make a little bet on toothpicks. Well, this was alright, too, because betting on toothpicks was what people were doing back then. Even when a place was jammed, you could pick out a table and bet how many toothpicks were on it. It was a fad, like Ouija or sitting on flagpoles.

" 'Okay,' I said, 'that table back there against the wall. I'll say there are 55 picks in the little bottle.'

" 'Nope,' he tells me. 'There's 47 of them.'

"And that's how many there were. Exactly 47. I paid the guy off, but I didn't bet anymore because it smelled like a hustle. I just sat there with my drink, and more guys came in and he took them the same way he took me. Pretty soon I saw how he was doing it. Everytime someone took a toothpick out of one of the bottles, this guy would pull out a notebook and make a record of it. He had come in there early in the day and counted every toothpick in every bottle. Every single toothpick in that speak, he had it counted. He was keeping a perpetual inventory of the toothpicks in this

90

place. It didn't matter what table a sucker chose, this guy knew to the sliver how many picks were on it. To this day, I've never bet on another toothpick.

And that's how Nick the Greek, a very pleasant fellow to talk with, once got took on toothpicks. And just so I can say that I've really benefited from the advice of a professional, let it be known that I also have refrained from any reckless betting on toothpicks.

CHAPTER NINE

My second trip to Jackson prison — for violating every parole rule, according to the authorities — was noteworthy mainly because of its brevity. As soon as the gates clanged shut behind me, I was almost physically overwhelmed by a feeling that I had never been anyplace except inside those gray walls. It was as though there were no world but this one, as though my first sentence had begun at some remote point in the past and was now continuing, without interruption, toward some unimaginable point in infinity. I didn't like that feeling even a little bit.

The obvious answer was to get out of it, to escape back to the world of people and good, solid reality. So I began planning my escape even before they had me in a cell. Once I had reached that stage, being back in prison wasn't so bad — because I knew I was as good as gone.

But going from Jackson prison is no easy thing. It's a maximum-security institution. That makes it tough to get out of, and even tougher to *stay* out of since escapes are rare and attract altogether too much attention. The only way around that was to have myself transferred to the minimum custody of a prison work camp. So I began immediately to angle for such a transfer.

I cooperated with the prison officials in every way possible. I took their many evaluation tests, I mopped my cell every morning, I attended chapel, I expressed an eager interest in the group therapy sessions, and I made it generally known that I was a reformed fellow. My frontal assault on rehabilitation paid off handsomely. Two months after I walked through those front gates, I managed to get myself screened and classified for minimum custody. I was transferred from the main prison to a work camp in northern Michigan.

The first thing I needed for my escape, now that I was actually in a position where I could leave, was a trustworthy partner. It was going to be a long walk out of those Michigan woods, and once out of them I would have to make contacts for money, clothes, and safe transportation out of the state. If any of my own contacts fell through, it would be handy to have someone along who could supply reliable alternatives.

I found the man I was looking for in the person of one Marty Redmond. I had known him in Detroit, and I had served time with him during my first stretch in Jackson. He was jam-up; a man who could be trusted not to run off at the mouth under any circumstances. And that is a very rare quality. People of that cut are scarce enough in the free world; in a prison population of 5,000 men you can generally count them on your fingers.

Among all the creepy people I met in my prowlings, the creepiest of all were the stoolies — and I mean the whole rotten lot of them; the idiots who confide their business and yours, if they find out about it, to all their goofy friends. They're part-time cops, swine who curry favor with information both false and true, animals who fink out just for the fun of it on things that don't in any way concern them. The whole rotten lot. And that's a lot, indeed. In recent years, the underworld has become increasingly overrun with these types to the extent that you can't be sure of having a solid accomplice even if you only go on jobs with your own mother. But myths about the Brotherhood of Crime and the Criminal Code are so persistent among honest johns that Joe Valachi himself couldn't dispel them.

On a per capita basis, very few stoolies actually get shot or dumped in rivers. But they do get jammed up in some ridiculous situations. There was a rat I heard about in New York who fingered an upcoming jewelry-store heist to eliminate his competition — then got mixed up, robbed the place himself, and was picked up on his own tip. A perfect example of just desserts coming home to roost. And since finks are regarded as villains even in politely square society, I thought I would throw that in to lend a nice moral tone to these revelations.

One reason for my confidence in Marty was that he had developed an almost pathological hatred of finks. When I first knew him, he was doing time for an armed robbery on which he'd been fingered by a guy named Izzy. Marty had been fingered before, and he regarded stoolies pretty much as a hazard of the trade. But his outrage at Izzy's perfidy knew no bounds. Izzy had been a friend. No one had paid Izzy, or threatened him with a prison sentence if he refused to talk, or slapped him around in the back of a station house until his mouth went to flapping. He had simply turned informer in order to feel important. And he was, as

94

Marty pointed out, nothing but a frigging fink without scruple one. Izzy had not only informed, he had systematically set Marty up for the bust. With seductive tales of a $10,000 score, he had talked him into pulling the job. Then he fingered the job to the police. And *then* he got right up on the witness stand and testified against Marty.

In prison, Marty would turn a livid blue at the mention of Izzy's name. Sometimes it seemed the only thing that kept him going was the thought of what he would do to Izzy when he got out of prison. At various times he claimed that he would shoot him, weight him down and drop him into the Detroit River, castrate him, strangle him, feed him rat poison, stab him, gouge out his eyeballs, throw him to the polar bears at the Detroit Zoo, burn him alive, cuss him to death, shatter his kneecaps with a Louisville Slugger, screw a C-clamp onto his skull, rope him to the chimes in the U of D Tower and ring him to death, dismember him an inch at a time with a GE electric carving knife, or, worst of all, get the snitching son-of-a-bitch bum-rapped into Jackson prison, where he could suffer the company of his own foul kind. Marty hated that Izzy something terrible.

One month before Marty was paroled, the Detroit Police found Izzy in the trunk of an abandoned car. He was, as the chaps in Jackson say, a regular lime popcicle — cold, green, and stiff. Naturally, Marty was heartbroken. Izzy's premature assassination not only did Marty out of the joy of maiming him personally, it also deprived him of the simple pleasures of anticipation. For two weeks he was inconsolable. He moped around the cell block, neglected his work, and spoke hardly a word.

Marty was a little radical, but at least I didn't have to worry about his mouth. So I was able to give my undivided attention to the problem of getting as far from the camp as possible, as fast as possible. The important thing in an escape is to get beyond the radius of the heat generated by your illegal departure and to stay out of sight until you have reached a point distant enough so that you will not be taken for an escaped convict merely because you are a stranger.

When the authorities noticed we were gone, of course, there would be an immediate manhunt. In Michigan, however, that isn't nearly such a terrible thing as the word implies. It simply means that the prison authorities notify the police and then send out a few state cars to patrol the nearby roads and highways. Neither the police nor the prison people ever bother getting out of their cars, and if a convict has enough sense to stay a couple of feet off the side of the road, there is virtually no possibility of being picked up by the patrols.

The summer before I got there, a friend of mine had taken off from the same camp. It was a regular textbook escape until he cut his foot on an old beer bottle while wading a stream. Deciding it would be smarter to turn himself in than to bleed to death, he made his way to the nearest highway and began waving down passing motorists. Not only did he fail to get a ride from any of the tourists, he was also ignored by three prison cars, two sheriff's patrols, and one state police car. He probably would have died right there on that highway if a couple of vacationing boy scouts hadn't helped him to the nearest village and summoned the constable.

My biggest concern wasn't for the road and highway patrols, or even for the other convicts who might notice our departure and snitch us off. It was for the farmers and Indians who lived in the surrounding country. Ordinarily, they were what you might call regular citizens; they feared

96

the Lord one day a week and sneered at the law all year round. They dumped their trash where they felt like dumping it, tore up roads and ordinances indiscriminately with their old Fords, robbed each other blind, took trout out of season, and ate venison three meals a day even in the summertime. They only turned each other in to the law when it was convenient. But let one poor, fleeing felon loose in the woods and they were all over him.

It wasn't civic-mindedness that brought these citizens out with their shotguns and deer rifles. It was plain, shabby greed. As soon as a man escapes from custody in Michigan, the state automatically puts a $50 reward on his head. Fifty lousy dollars! You can't even buy a decent load of garbage for $50. But it's more than enough to get you blown four ways from Wednesday by a Michigan farmer. Getting shot for a $1,000 reward is bad enough; but $50 is an insult, both to the felons and to the farmers. Whatever else he might have done, Judas surely ruined the price for Michigan.

In any event, we could count on a lot of armed locals sitting in their silos with field glasses. So we would have to stay well clear of all habitations, and we would have to stay alert enough to spot the poachers before they spotted us.

Marty and I spent a week figuring out the details of our escape — the route we would take, the tactics we would employ to avoid detection, who we might contact after we made it out of the woods, and what we would take with us. We decided to hold our supplies to a bare minimum; one razor between the two of us, so we could make ourselves presentable before we reached civilization, and a bag of cheese and crackers that Marty boosted from the camp kitchen.

Once we had ourselves organized, we didn't see any point

97

in giving Michigan any more of our valuable time. We chose a night when there was no moon and an entire herd of nightcows could have lost itself without a trace in the darkness of the woods. We slipped out of the barracks and trailed off toward freedom.

During the month of August, the wilds of northern Michigan are lush with thimbleberries, blackberries, wild strawberries, gooseberries, dingleberries, hackberries, elderberries, whortleberries, boysenberries and blueberries. There are chokecherries, wild plums, green apples, and peaches. There is wintergreen to sweeten the tired palate. And if there is anything of the gourmet about you, I have it on good authority that milkweed root is not to be excelled for sheer delicacy of flavor; unless, perhaps, you find yourself in some gentle swale where cattail shoots may be gathered. The woods abound with wild goodies, and no man need go hungry. Not unless he runs out of cheese and crackers.

Marty and I did alright for the first three days. Really, it was quite an idyllic escape. Wherever possible, we held to high ground and first growth timber. The woods were dark and cool, and the ground was covered with a deep, fragrant layer of pine needles. There was no undergrowth to speak of, only knee-high canebrakes, soft ferns that grew thick and even all through the woods like a pale, undulating billiard table.

Shortly before we took to the timber, I had been reading *Walden* and, still under the influence of Thoreau, was feeling very much the noble savage as we tramped through this sylvan wilderness. I think there was also a bit of James Fenimore Cooper mixed in there some place. I would have been well-content to imagine that forest stretching endlessly beyond the horizons — hundreds of trees, thousands even,

98

covering the continent from coast to coast, with nary a road or hamlet or policeman in the whole, vast extent of it. I still had the copy of *Walden* with me — a rather unidyllic and raggedy paperback — and occasionally I would dig it out of my hip pocket and leaf through it as we made rest stops to snack on cheese and crackers.

Even prosaic old Marty was caught up in the spell of the forest.

"Say, John," he said, "I been thinking. You know, this is just like Fess Parker marching through the Cumberland Gap, way back before there was even any gap there."

"Don't be silly," I said. "This is a prison escape and it's serious business. Don't go getting romantic about it."

To stretch our cheese supply, we had been picking berries as we went along. This was quite easy, if not very rewarding. We were picking on stragglers, lonely little bushes sprouting feebly where they had no business being, and the berries from these plants were sadly anemic. But we stripped each bush as we came to it, and in this manner probably managed to supplement our diet to the extent of two or three quarts a day. To the uninitiated, this may seem a large quantity of berries. Such is not the case. Pulpy, wee mites that they are, berries can be inhaled on peck at a time by even a small and mildly hungry man. They are not what you would call a robust and satisfying food. Half of their substance is lost between picking and eating in the rich juice that runs down your arms, attracting unbelievable numbers of flies, and turning you purple in spite of the most fastidious precautions. The rest of the berry is composed of indigestible seeds.

On our fourth day out, the cheese was almost gone, and Marty had fed our last cracker to a tufted titmouse. I didn't question his motives for doing so, as I knew him well enough to assume it was nothing more than an innocent flight of fancy. But we only had enough cheese left to have one ounce apiece for supper. It was necessary to begin foraging for real.

The bounty of nature is never so conspicuously meager as when you are hungry. Until our rations ran out, I had been entertaining notions of snaring rabbits, killing partridges by means of stones that I intended to hurl with terrible accuracy, and perhaps even bushwhacking a deer with an improved shillelagh. That stuff is okay when you are sitting beneath a tree with a bag of crackers and pretending it's Walden Pond. In desperate practice, however, none of the meat running around in those woods wanted to hold still long enough to be eaten. We didn't see one deer all the time we were in the woods. Now and then we found their footprints, or heard them crashing off through the undergrowth where the woods were thick, but they never let us get close enough for a good peek, not to mention a rap between the eyes. Obviously they were not cut from the same litter as the antlered bums that hung around the prison camp mooching cookies from the guys in the barracks.

Snaring rabbits also proved to be a gross impossibility. Neither Marty nor I knew how to fashion a snare. And if we had, we would have had to sit around waiting for a rabbit to come along who was stupid enough to stick his head in it. Waiting in the bushes is not an easy or a pleasant thing when you are hungry and in a hurry to get the hell out of the woods.

The partridges just laughed and flew away. I nearly wrenched my arm out of joint trying to hang a rock on one of the beggars, but it was no use. And Marty only managed to hit himself in the knee when one of his missiles ricocheted back from a pine stump.

100

My experience with the trout was the most disillusioning of all. For many years I had cherished a notion that it was possible to catch fish with one's bare hands. I had talked with wise old men who claimed to have accomplished this feat, and I had read innumerable accounts of others doing the same thing. There was Running Deer, the proud Sioux warrior, who was reputedly able to snatch dozens of fish out of the swiftest stream; there was Phineas Coffin, renegade son of a Nantucket whaler, who thought nothing of capturing Columbia River salmon by pinching their gills shut; there was Fess Parker himself. All of these hunters used the same general technique. They would stretch themselves out on a ledge of rock or a tree limb overhanging a stream. Then they would cautiously reach down into the water and tickle their prey on the stomach. According to Phineas Coffin and other authorities, fish are so enamoured of this sort of fondling that they are charmed into rigid immobility and will allow themselves to be lifted from the water without the smallest objection.

There have been a number of delightful occasions when I have found it charming to be tickled on the stomach. I have also tickled a few stomachs in my time and induced varying states of bliss in the ticklees — but none of these stomachs, be it noted, belonged to fish. Fish simply do not get their jollies the same way people get theirs. From my own observations, in fact, I would say that a fish definitely resents any attempts at fondling its stomach. There are, perhaps, a few repressed people around who share the fish's antagonism to stomach fondling — but I have yet to meet a fish broadminded enough to accept the more widely current human point of view.

Michigan trout streams are not well suited to the titillation of stomachs in the first place. Rocky ledges are rare in

101

the lower peninsula, and the banks of the streams are heavily overgrown with shrubbery. With much determination and
a sharp machete, you can force your way through this
growth and reach the stream. But before you ever get clear
of the bushes you are already waist deep in icy water and
quite at a loss for anything to stretch out on. Where the
banks are not hopelessly jungled, they are usually composed
of deep, black muck. The sportsmen who wade these
streams in rubber boots like to call the stuff quicksand, because it makes them feel adventuresome. Sticky, stinking
and inconvenient it may be, but still just ordinary muck —
and rotten for tickling purposes.

Eventually, Marty and I found a spot beneath a railroad
trestle where a pile of ties gave convenient access to a
stream. Stretched out on the ties, we could peer down into
a deep pool full of the shadowy, drifting shapes of trout.
There were at least a dozen of them, ranging from one to
three pounds; all those lean, firm-fleshed fish, ours for the
tickling.

But the fish would have none of it. They were as skittish
as a flock of schoolgirls on their first hayride. Perhaps if I
could have gotten one alone . . . . but no matter; they were
not schoolgirls, and neither blandishments nor stealth were
to any effect. I held my arm submerged and motionless until it turned numb from the cold. Running Deer would have
been proud of my stoicism. Still, the fish held themselves
suspiciously aloof in the dim corners where they had first
fled, coldly hostile toward my unmoving hand.

Marty had a go at the fish, too, and I think the total failure of his efforts, combined with severe hunger, must have
left lasting scars on his psyche. Some years later, when we
were both free and unencumbered by "wanted" posters, I
occasionally ran into Marty at a Detroit bar where the own-

ers had installed an aquarium of tropical fish. Everytime Marty got half gassed he would climb up on the bar, reach into the tank without even taking his coat off, and begin chasing guppies, gouramis, and tetras from one end of the tank to the other. Whenever he managed to catch one before he was ejected, he would hold the unfortunate beast in one hand and stroke its stomach with the other.

"Smile, you son-of-a-bitch," he would coo at the fish. "Smile just once before I chew the ass right off you!"

Since it was evident that the wildlife was not going to cooperate with our appetites, we conceded defeat at the trestle and resigned ourselves to a vegetable diet. We began with what we sincerely hoped was an elderberry bush and stripped it naked. The berries didn't taste remotely like elderberry wine, but they were at least palatable. We topped these off with wild strawberries which were sweet and delicious, but small and sparse. We had no choice but to keep moving.

I think it was Marty who first came up with the idea of picking mushrooms. Hungry as I was, I would have been receptive to the suggestion that we look for candied violets. But the idea of mushrooms was loaded with connotations of thick steaks, savory soups, and gourmet delights. It was a great idea! The woods were crawling with mushrooms, and we could eat like kings all the way back to civilization.

Presently, Marty fell to rummaging in the humus. When he stood up he was triumphantly flourishing a mushroom that resembled a small sponge.

"Aha!" he cried, presenting me with the mushroom, "a morel. They're absolutely delicious."

I accepted the spongy-looking thing and squinted closely

103

at it before dropping it in my pocket and wiping my hands on my trousers.

"Fine," I said. "Better see if we can pick up a few more. Can't make a meal on one mushroom, you know."

"Right."

Marty got down on all fours and began digging through the carpet of needles and leaves. I did the same.

"Here's three more," said Marty, crawling over and handing them to me. "We're not going to have to wait to cook these, you know. We can eat them raw."

"Right," I said, quickly stuffing them into my pocket with the first one.

Before long I spotted five of the sponges protruding through the pine needles. I snapped them off gingerly and handed them to Marty.

"There you go, Marty. We're doing pretty good, eh boy?"

"Yeah," he said, dropping the mushrooms in his pocket. "Maybe we'll do better if we look a little farther along."

So we wandered on through the woods, looking for bigger and better herds of mushrooms. We hadn't gone far before Marty bent down and plucked something from the shadow of a bush.

"Saaay," he said, "here's a good one for you. Saw a picture of one just like it in a magazine once."

Reluctantly, I accepted the offering. It was a bright orange, with evil whitish pimples and eruptions all over it. I stuffed the colorful fungus in my pocket with the others. I had no intention of eating it.

We had gone only a little ways further when I spied a smooth cheeked little fellow about four inches tall. There wasn't a wart on it. It was plump and meaty, a velvety fawn color with white gills. This one actually *looked* edible. On the other hand, it could be one of nature's nasty little tricks.

104

That innocent and comely exterior could well mask a heart as lethal as a cup of hemlock. I tossed it to Marty, covertly watching him with a keen, clinical interest.

"Here you go, Marty boy. Finest specimen I've seen in a long time."

Marty gave me a pained look and stuffed the mushroom into his pocket. I very much suspected that he had no intention of eating it.

Neither of us said anything more about looking for mushrooms. We carried the ones we had already collected for each other until that evening. By that time they were in pretty bad shape from being kept so long in our pockets, and we both agreed that it was a rotten shame we had let them go so long and that we might as well throw them away.

The following morning we were both so hungry that we imagined ourselves borderline starvation cases. Getting out of the woods now was entirely secondary to finding something to eat. Our only course was to find huge quantities of berries, the only things we had yet found that might be depended upon as a source of food. So we began looking in earnest for a berry patch.

Berry patches grow in the sunlight, where it is hot and sticky. They flourish in clearings, and they surround stands of timber with impenetrable, brambly barriers of thorn. When we came out of the woods at noon, we waded straight into an acre of knotted and prickly blackberry bushes. The air above them was hazy with covens of midges, gnats, bees, wasps, deer flies, and yellow jackets. Everything hummed and thrummed and whined with a million wings. And the bushes were fat with berries.

Marty and I began picking and eating berries faster than the insects could abandon them. We didn't even get that much meat in the stew back at camp. Until nearly sundown,

105

we swatted flying things, sweated, itched, prickled, and bled from countless scratches. But we ate berries!

If the authorities had found us then they probably wouldn't have wanted us back. Both of us were covered with welts and purple stains. Even our hair was matted flat with crushed berries. Our clothing was shredded, and by the time we were through we were both shirtless, having removed them to improvise berry baskets. We were bloated and very nearly sick — but we weren't hungry.

We carried our soggy and berry-laden shirts back to higher ground in the woods where we would be less at the mercy of mosquitoes, and we sat up most of the night eating more berries.

In the morning, we dined on berries again. Neither of us was very enthusiastic over the menu by then, but we couldn't waste time looking for another berry patch later. We had to get out of that part of the country as fast as we could. So we went back to our thorny larder and ate ourselves to the near side of nausea. Then we loaded our shirts again and resumed our trek toward civilization.

The last of the berries were gone by noon — and with them almost went aglimmering our hopes of escape. We were sitting in a swamp, catching our breath and idly wondering which way was North, when I felt the first cramps. Within 20 minutes, I was doubled up with severe abdominal pains, and Marty wasn't far behind in coming down with the same symptoms. We both had acute cases of what is politely known as dysentery. Actually, it was pure, unleavened fruitarrhea. Never in the annals of prison escapes have there been two such classic cases of that undignified indisposition.

If the law could have picked up our trail at that point, they would have had no trouble following us blindfolded for the next 24 hours. We left a spoor that would have done credit to a herd of panic-stricken elephants. Our progress, after that first stop, was measured in dashes of 100 yards or so — and dashing is no easy matter when expediency demands that you don't pull your trousers all the way up.

The next morning, with all hope of sleep long forgotten, I looked over at Marty crouched down behind a bush. His shirt was gone, he was caked with dirt and blood and stain and his eyes were sloppy red puddles. He looked like the smallest raisin in the litter after it's been worked over by a hill of ravenous ants. He was a damn mess.

Marty looked sadly over at me. In a strained tone, he said:

"This is the one, Goddamnedest stinking escape I've ever been on."

And, crouching there on my own side of that bush, I couldn't help but agree with him.

CHAPTER TEN

There is a thing in this country known as "a visible means of support" and, as free as our system is supposed to be, you can find yourself in a great deal of trouble if you don't have one. Respectable citizens don't often run into the problem, because they usually have gainful employment and they are known in their communities. If they venture into strange places it is most often in the role of tourists; spenders of money who are making welcome contributions to someone else's visible means of support. But it's a different thing altogether for the penniless or the larcenous. The old knight of the road ideal is long dead — try hoboing your way around the country today, and it will get you nothing but a tedious succession of vagrancy arrests. And just let the local fuzz find out you've got a record. Man, there's nothing in this world that draws more heat than an out-of-town hoodlum — unless it's a man who is wanted for prison escape. And that was me.

Marty, for all I knew, was still trying to make it on the

108

lam in Michigan. But, after getting a friend to drive me to Chicago and catching a plane for the coast, I was safely in California, faced with two basic requirements for remaining safe: I had to avoid all underworld associations, and I had to have a visible means of support.

The first part was easy. I stayed away from known hangouts, and I took a room at the Y in San Francisco. I had avoided heat on previous occasions by staying at the Y.M.C.A. It's really not such a bad deal. There is a sitting room where you can write letters on Y.M.C.A. stationery, engage in wholesome conversation with other Christians, and read your Bible. The infrequent plainclothesman who comes through is only looking for faggots, and if you keep a stiff wrist about you, you're never bothered.

With lodging out of the way, I began prowling through the papers to see what might be available in the way of undemanding employment. I was already one-up on the situation, because I didn't care a twit about the wages. After you've been a thief for a certain length of time, you almost come to regard yourself as independently wealthy. What I was looking for was a job that would require the smallest possible investment of time. One that I might be able to ride along on for a couple of months before being officially canned.

The ideal job for a thief, under these circumstances, is working as a commission salesman, because your employer never expects you to make any money. This had already worked beautifully for me in Chicago, and even once in Detroit, when a particularly unpleasant parole officer had threatened to send me back to prison if I didn't show evidence of gainful employment. These are also the easiest types of jobs to find. You just look for an ad by one of those outfits that promises to show you how to earn up to $50 a day in your spare time. Then you give the people ten dollars, and they give you a fistful of printed propaganda and a sample case containing a lot of high-class merchandise like SHINO, a guaranteed magic polish that does equally well on silverware or Mack trucks. For all the income you can expect from trying to sell this junk, you might as well eat it. But it is a visible means of support, so far as the law is concerned; a perfect excuse for having the money from your last holdup or burglary.

I was prepared, however, to seek a position somewhat more substantial. One that might pay a decent wage and also offer opportunities for larceny. I wasn't entirely unqualified for honest labor. Professional thieves — like professional whores — often have a fling at going straight. I was no exception. A few times, I simply stopped stealing for a while and lived on what I'd accumulated until I got hungry enough to go back to work. But there were times when I actually sought out legitimate employment. Although I was never notably successful at such efforts, these infrequent spasms of honesty (which, somehow, always seemed to coincide with paroles) landed me jobs as a TV announcer, ad man, used-car salesman, draftsman, and truck driver. I was even a professional crucifier. For two weeks, I held a job with an organization that manufactured crucifixes. My function was to nail the little gold and silver plated Christs to the eight-inch crosses that came in a choice of ebony, rosewood, walnut, and cherry. The next time it falls your lot to crucify someone in this world, let me suggest that it will be easiest to nail him to cherry.

But for San Francisco I wanted something better, and to this end I made a thorough search of the classifieds. I found what I was looking for in an ad placed by a Mr. R.W. Thurgood, who was looking for a French tutor for his two sons, aged 12 and 14. My knowledge of French at the time, and I'm the first to admit it, was limited to basic grammar and base vocabulary. Very base, indeed. I'd picked up most of it from a French sailor who had once shared a cell with me in the Wayne County jail. My pronunciation would have driven a bulldog off a meat wagon. The important thing, though, was that Thurgood had enough money to hire a tutor. That being the case, it behooved me to have a go at offering whatever might pass for my services.

Armed with two of the most beautiful letters of recommendation that ever had been hurriedly written on Y.M.C.A. typewriters, and with a copy of Proust casually protruding from my coat pocket, I caught a cab out to the Thurgood residence in the Pacific Heights section. This was my kind of territory — huge old houses and sprawling lawns that oozed money from every expensively maintained square inch. Many thieves cut a wide path around neighborhoods like this, because it's commonly assumed that the very wealthy are difficult to rob — a frightful misconception that has caused many a poor crook to pass up a bountiful score. In spite of their burglar alarms and their private police forces, the rich are far more easily gulled than the man who sweats for an ordinary income.

Old Thurgood, for instance, didn't even bother to read my letters of recommendation. He gave me a drink of excellent brandy and asked about my background. I gave him a straightforward bit of guff about my studies at the Sorbonne, my assistant professorship at Wellesley, and my Rhodes scholarship. It was an altogether disgraceful story to hang on any mark, but he sucked it all up and begged for more. So I told him how I was using my sabbatical to finish work on a definitive biography of Pierre Louys, but thought I might pick up a little supplemental income through tutor-

111

ing. We scholars, you know, receive such miserly recompense for our efforts. And who, in these days of crass commercialism, really appreciates scholarship at its true value? Thurgood, for one. He took me on for three lessons a week at $30 a session.

I couldn't have lasted very long at the job, of course, but, as it turned out, I didn't have to. The kids were no more interested in French than I was, so we sat around for a couple of weeks listening to their rock-and-roll records while I sucked up the old man's brandy and taught the kids how to be articulately profane in French. And before my ignorance could become entirely manifest, I had worked up a most promising relationship with the woman who owned the adjoining property. Her name was Millicent, and she was a widow in her middle 50's, a charming old doll with a lubricous urge for younger men. She was afflicted with incipient dowager's hump, which made her look a little like a toadstool, and she had a neck like a turkey. But these shortcomings were coupled with a great many endearing qualities that made her well-nigh irresistible. Not the least among these qualities was money.

Milly was legitimate; not a secretary who had worked her way up, or an ex-madam who had scuffled for her loot the hard way. She had sedately and tastefully inherited it from her grandfather, who had made his fortune in arch supports, hernia pads, suppositories, and all the other cheap nostrums that get advertised in the back of comic books. Milly wouldn't talk about her grandfather, but she was obviously square enough to be talked out of his money.

Milly was also a member in good standing (unaccustomed as she was to that position) of the Chamber of Commerce, and she was a director for a leading civic museum. Her social and financial contacts were beyond reproach. Among her many friends there were still such things as Wrong Forks, Unacceptable Accents, Poor Tailoring, Gauche Displays, Nouveau Richeness and Deficient Family. Milly provided me with a first-class "in" to a social stratum that otherwise would have been closed to me. Dear, dear Milly. Did I hang a lot of checks on her snooty friends? Did I steal the gold spigots from their marble bathtubs? You bet I did!

One week after I met Milly I became a kept man. I abandoned Thurgood's nursery in favor of Milly's quattrocento boudoir. And to compensate me for the sacrifice of my scholarly pursuits, not to mention my fair white body, the old doll fitted me out with a complete wardrobe that would see me through any of the social events she was so fond of. It was at one of these functions that I pulled off my best sting on the coast — at the same time that Milly scored her most notable social achievement.

The affair in question was a birthday party for a San Francisco industrialist, and it was held in the back yard of a home that was damn near shingled with cash. There were nearly 100 guests present, all elegant folk from the Social Register, and nobody had to bring his own booze, because the host had the stuff stacked on tables at handy spots around the yard. I thought that was an especially nice touch of class. But I was more impressed by the larceny potential of the joint. Before being escorted out to the garden by a uniformed maid, Milly and I were ushered upstairs to the johns, where we were encouraged to refresh ourselves from the rigors of the one-mile drive it had taken to get from Milly's place to this one. Pure elegance. Not feeling any pressing need for refreshment, I lingered in the hallway to see where the maid went with Milly's purse and mink stole.

All the guests' goodies, I learned, were being deposited

in what seemed to be the master bedroom. And I mean, man, it was jammed with goodies. Fat purses stacked all over the place, and more expensive furs than you could find this side of a Hudson's Bay trading post. It had all the makings of a lovely party.

Outside, Milly and I mingled with the other guests, and I picked up a drink but didn't work on it much because my attention was bent on the problem of getting to that room upstairs. The only way into the house was across the rear terrace and through the kitchen, where two maids were busily engaged in the endless preparation of hors d'oeuvres, and it was purely impossible to get past them without being seen. I mulled the situation over and decided to wait a while and see how things shaped up later in the evening. If the circumstances didn't improve, I could always take a chance on quietly smashing in one of the side windows.

By the time the party was three hours old, most of the elegant guests were elegantly snockered, and I was sort of sorry I hadn't kept up with them on the booze intake, as the action in the shrubbery seemed to be getting rather interesting — middle-aged nymphets dashing about, fairies in the bottom of the garden, and all that. Take your pick. From a lawn chair on the terrace, where I could peek into the kitchen from time to time to check on the maids, I could see Milly lushing it up with three of her girl friends. They were standing beside a marble fish pond that was being used to chill wine, and they were devoting an unseemly amount of attention to the fountain that fed the pond; a boyish bronze satyr, urinating archly into the mixed bag of goldfish and Chablis. The filter on the pump system was evidently in bad shape, because every few minutes the stream of water would diminish and trickle to a halt. Whenever this happened, Milly and her friends would giggle, clap the little chap on his back, and vigorously kick the pedestal to rattle loose the accumulation of rusty silt and restore the flow.

I was almost ready to try my luck on that side window when I noticed that the old girls by the fountain were giving the little satyr a rougher than usual workout. Three of them were thumping away at the pedestal, while Milly was hammering the general vicinity of the bladder with a croquet mallet. And all to no avail. The flow seemed to have petered out permanently.

And that's when Milly made the party. Backing off to one side to get range for a full swing with the mallet, Millie took one step too many. Arms flailing, mallet sailing, Millie tumbled into the pond. She landed on her back among the fishies, displacing lilypads and bottles, and successfully showering her three friends and several other guests who were standing nearby. All conversation stopped as Millie thrashed to her feet in the shallow water.

The silence was so great that the two maids from the kitchen came out on the terrace to see what was happening, and that was just the opportunity I needed. While everyone watched the mermaid disport herself, I slipped through the kitchen door and hot-footed it up the service stairs.

After the diversion that made it possible, my score was almost an anticlimax. I went straight to the master bedroom and loaded up a bedspread with everything it would hold — ten of the most expensive looking furs, cash and jewelry from nearly three dozen purses, and the contents of a large jewel box that I found in the room. I had to pass up more than I like to think about, but the stuff that I had made one hell of a pile, and it took me a quarter of an hour to collect it.

Before leaving the room with my cumbersome bundle of loot, I unlocked a window that opened onto a sun deck and

115

threw it wide open. Then I sprinted down the front stairs, glanced into the living room and the study to make sure they were empty, and went out through the front door, locking it behind me.

I locked the goodies in the trunk of Milly's Lincoln and strolled back around the side of the house just in time to comfort a dripping Milly for the kidding she was taking from her girl friends. I'm always considerate that way. Besides, I was sincerely indebted to her for the help she had given me.

I stayed with Milly for two months, making regular stings on her friends without once getting a rumble. I picked up jewelry and loose cash from their homes, I stuck them with checks that I guaranteed to make good, I touched them for loans, and I sold one of Milly's cars and two gold spigots. I got those without even having to use a pipe wrench. They are so easy to steal that whenever anyone asks me if he should install gold spigots in his home I tell him hell no.

There wasn't much choice about leaving Milly. I had too many checks coming due, her friends were becoming increasingly upset with me, and Milly's demands for attention were becoming downright debilitating. So I bought an old car and headed south. And that's when things stopped being good to me in California.

Some miles below Los Angeles, there is a region given over to the cultivation of citrus crops. The countryside is peaceful and lovely — and a million miles away from that Michigan prison camp and the scores I'd been knocking off up in San Francisco. And for a sad little time I didn't even think of those things. That was a sorry mistake.

In my carefree way, I stopped at a roadside tavern for a bottle of beer. Midway through the beer, I fell into a conversation with a local chap, and the talk drifted around to

116

farming fruit in general and labor problems in particular. I knew nothing at all about fruit, but when this farmer mentioned the wages he was paying his Mexican labor, I allowed as how it seemed to me that the tightest hillbilly plantation owner in Mississippi would pay more than that to an industrious boll weevil. And, after delivering myself of that observation, I found that I had no choice but to fight the idiot.

It's a basic rule for a man wanted by the law that he should not put himself in a situation where he will attract the law's attention. I violated this rule — rather badly and very stupidly. While the management-type farmer and I were still trying to kick in each other's ribs, a sheriff's patrol pulled up in front of the tavern. The farmer, who was on a first-name basis with the arresting officers, was sent home to lick his multiple contusions. And I — alas, poor I — I was carried off to still another of the many jails of my life.

The bull pen in this particular jail enjoyed the distinction of being the longest and skinniest I'd ever seen. At one time, it had apparently been a service corridor that gave access to another wing of the building. Sixty-feet long and four-feet wide, it had been converted to a bull pen by walling off one end with brick and installing a barred door at the other. The accommodations consisted of nine double-deck bunks, arranged end to end along one wall, and a large, lidded slop bucket. Since there was only a foot of space between the beds and the wall, the authorities had been thoughtful enough to provide a rectangular bucket especially tailored to fit. It was two-feet tall, three-feet long, and ten-inches wide. It was constructed of galvanized metal, with extremely ragged edges. To accomplish anything on this horror without being castrated, a man had to chin him-

117

self on an upper bunk and pray fervently that the bed didn't collapse.

I took an immediate liking to the undersheriff in command of this bastille because he was not dressed like Hoot Gibson. His garb was more in the fashion of Lash LaRue, hero of my pre-adolescence, complete with concho belt, sombrero, and a grande vest. He also took a liking to me, presumably because his Spanish was as rotten as mine, and I was the only customer who could speak a passable brand of English.

On my first day in the bull pen, Lash summoned me to his desk in the adjoining office and bluntly revealed his life's passion — a game called "Battleship." I knew all about it, having played it continuously all through the eighth grade at three different schools. Two people are needed to play, each with a large sheet of paper divided into squares that are numbered down the left margin and lettered alphabetically across the top. The players secretly mark the positions of battleships, cruisers, and destroyers on their own grids, deploying their fleets in a random pattern. Then they take turns calling out grid designations, and whenever one of these corresponds with the position of an opponent's ship, that ship is considered lost. This merriment continues until one of the players has lost his entire fleet.

If you are really freaked on the game, there are any number of additional refinements that can be dragged in to complicate things, everything from alloting a different number of points for the various classes of warships to keeping a double grid, one for your own ships and the other for recording your salvos and plotting the position of the enemy fleet.

Lash was not only freaked on the game, he was a raving fanatic. The entire surface of his desk — a scarred and ancient thing of oak, that measured four-by-six feet and seemed to be imbedded in the flooring — was covered by a grid of one-inch squares that he had carefully ruled off with blue paint. It came complete with tiny, gray plastic ship models, evidently the residue of many long ago boxes of Crispy Crunchies. The layout had a suspiciously permanent look about it, and I could readily see where this nut's obsession could turn into a real drag.

Did I know anything about Battleship? Not on your life. I demurred. I denied any intimacy with boats of any description. And such obviously deep and complicated games were far beyond my comprehension.

But Lash was devoted to his madness, and he succeeded, at length, in convincing me of the beauties of the game. There was the rich tapestry of naval tradition spread out before us on the grid; the subtleties of warfare at sea; the challenge of competition; the crossing of the T; the excitement of having one's flagship blown from beneath one's feet; the satisfaction of laying a 16-inch projectile on the other man's deck; the pure Sturm und Drang of the seascape; the three meals a day that I would be fed only on condition that I played the Goddamned game.

After he had gone over the rules of his game in meticulous detail, Lash returned me to the bull pen and furnished me with a large, shapeless lump of blue chalk. It was the same crumbling sort of stuff that carpenters use for drawing dirty pictures on floor joists, and it was far from ideal for deploying battleships. But pencils were forbidden in the bull pen. Many of my Mexican cellmates, it turned out, were dope addicts. At some time in his life, Lash had read a pile of tabloid literature about junkies, and he was convinced that in their terrible desperation they would seize upon any pointed object to gouge open their veins. He had visions of

119

heroin being poured into bloodstreams. Scandalous narcotics orgies right there in his beautiful little jail.

Working with my back wedged against the bunks, I became admiral of a grid-lined ocean sea that extended from floor to ceiling for half the length of the bull pen. It was necessary to make my ocean 48 squares high and 72 squares long, so that it would conform exactly to the one Lash was using. And I had to do it without a straightedge, using that clumsy, flaking clot of chalk, stumbling over beds, the bucket, Mexicans, and my own feet.

Lash and I played one game of Battleship every day. Each game lasted from early in the morning until late in the afternoon, and it wasn't unusual for Lash to work overtime in order to see the last ship sent to the bottom. Those sinkings took longer than the uninitiated might suspect. We each started out with 20 battleships, 40 cruisers, and 70 destroyers. That was our stock fleet. Depending on how many interruptions he anticipated, Lash might also stock our oceans with aircraft carriers, mine sweepers, PT boats, and up to 100 submarines apiece. A force of that magnitude, I can tell you, takes a weary lot of sinking.

The scale-model warfare was more grueling than the real thing ever thought of being. I tended to be systematic in my firing, and usually concentrated on blotting out all the squares in one particular area of ocean. Saturation shelling, as it were. But Lash was a bracket man. From his flagship in the adjoining office he would call out, "ZZT-1!" indicating, with a grid designation that he'd invented himself, the top, right-hand square. For anything in the top ten rows, I had to climb into an upper bunk to reach the square and mark the small cross that showed where the shell had landed. His next salvo would land in A-48, sending me scrambling across bunks, Mexicans, and that reeking bucket to reach the lower left-hand corner.

And all the pointless scrambling in that meaningless game was rendered still more pointless by the certain knowledge that I was not going to win. No matter where I called my shots in those three thousand, four hundred and fifty-six squares, Lash always had half his fleet intact when the last of mine had gone to the bottom. Every evening after the last gun was stilled, Lash would take me into the office to gauge for myself the extent of his victory. And more than once, after hours of methodically wiping out his squares, I found two thirds of his fleet improbably huddled on the last 100 squares remaining untouched.

Those three weeks I spent with the Lash LaRue Navy are with me yet. Just as I did every night in that bull pen, in fact, I still see an occasional grid pattern in my sleep. It's impossible to forget the hazy unreality of the endless games. Forbidden the wickedness of pencils, my Mexican cellmates were smuggling pot by the bushel into the bull pen. And between the joints they were giving me and the contact high I was picking up while chasing my squares across the wall, I managed to keep just enough of a grip on myself to avoid falling into the slop bucket.

The fact that I was turning a delicate cerulean from the chalk dust did nothing to steady my grip. During my time in the bull pen, I used up four pounds of chalk. Walls, floor, cast iron castrater, goofy Mexicans, and stoned me, we all turned bluer than a tribe of frozen Picts.

When I finally got loose from that madhouse, I was still high and halfway convinced that another jailer with a bigger desk must have called out, "ZZU-49", mercifully moving me off the lower right-hand corner of the grid and clear the hell out of California.

121

And that's about the way it was. The bigger jailer was J. Edgar Hoover. He had gotten around to matching my fingerprints with my escape warrant. I was on my way back to Michigan, to finish the prison sentence I had almost forgotten.

CHAPTER ELEVEN

Until I walked out of prison again, with my escape sentence and the balance due on my original sentence safely behind me, I had scarcely given a thought to what I was going to do for a living. I began thinking about it in earnest only when I got on the bus that was taking me back to Detroit.

Somehow, the old hustles didn't appeal to me any more. Petty crime was entertaining enough, and it could provide a fair income, but the law of averages was always stepping on your heels. You had to steal too frequently, exposing yourself to a possible arrest every time. And the more often you were pinched, the more likely you were to draw a conviction. So petty crime was out. And so was the possibility of going back to work for the mob. There was too much politics mixed up in the numbers racket — and there's nothing in this world that corrupts a good racket more surely than politics.

An honest job was out of the question, of course. So far

out that it didn't even occur to me as a stopgap measure. But, just at that moment, I couldn't think of a single dishonest occupation that really grabbed me. Then I thought of the man who was sitting two seats in front of me. He was another ex-con, who had been released from prison with me that same morning. His beef was armed robbery. He wasn't especially bright, but he'd been pulling holdups, off and on, for close to ten years before taking his first bust. That didn't sound bad at all. The more I thought about it, in fact, the more it appealed to me. A good armed robber can live very well just by taking off one or two scores a month — always with the possibility of grabbing an especially ripe job that will allow him an extended vacation on the Riviera.

I sat counting the hairs on the back of that holdup man's neck most of the way to Detroit. I thought of all the jobs that goof had pulled without getting caught. And I thought how nice life could be if I didn't have to risk going back to prison every time I picked up $50 or $100 on a short hustle. By the time the bus had passed through Ann Arbor and Ypsilanti, I was feeling as though the shade of Jesse James were sitting at my side, urging me to abandon my old ways and to get into a business more in keeping with my talents. Going through Wayne, I was almost sure that God was speaking to me through that stubbly neck up ahead. And by the time I reached my stop in Detroit, I had made up my mind.

Armed robbery taught me more about crime and life and people than all the combined hustles I'd ever thought of pulling. And it taught me a lot about myself. It also taught me that you don't commit a serious crime unless you approach it in the right frame of mind — not if you want to succeed.

124

Having approached many jobs with varying degrees of success, I can vouch that the proper frame probably lies someplace between reserved confidence and trouser-wetting terror. Unpleasant though it may be, that last element is vitally important. The wonderful Sarah Bernhardt once commented to an understudy who had been boasting that she didn't know the meaning of stage fright, "Wait until you're a performer, my dear, and you'll find out." Similarly, the late and wonderful Mad Dog Coll is known to have cautioned a nerveless young accomplice, "Ignernt punk! Ya better git scairt or I'll lace ya up with this here chopper."

Occupational panic, you see, is common to all the performing arts — to actors who take the stage to mutilate the bard, to salesmen who tell shameless lies in public, to politicians who make the salesmen look good and honorable, and to armed robbers who are always guaranteed a hostile audience, and press reviews that will be disparaging at best. The panic, the acid knot in the gut, is what keeps them honest and true to the devious course they have set for themselves.

I've known bandits who suffered from stage fright to such an extent that they couldn't eat for two or three days before the score. Harry Zelnick habitually went on jobs in such a state of distraction that he often forgot to zip his fly. And I once knew a forger who got so nervous when he was passing checks that his victims used to run around getting him ammonia inhalers and glasses of water, thinking he was going to faint. On one job he did just that; swooned dead away. And when they dug out his wallet to look for his next of kin, they found six different sets of identification — which earned him seven to 14 years in state prison.

But nothing can beat a robbery for the sheer drama of personal confrontation. And I was always fascinated by the

125

many different ways that people react to that drama. The stress of the situation, the element of danger, and the pure, classic conflict of elements in the circumstances provide a perfect setting for the study of human response. It's entirely possible that my interest in this has lessened my effectiveness as an armed bandit, but I've learned much from my observations. And, in the long run, I believe the lessons in human nature are worth almost as much as the loot I've picked up.

There was the time, for instance, when I went on a savings-and-loan company heist in Chicago with a couple of friends. It was a typically rotten December afternoon. A cold north wind, loaded with slop and sleet, was blowing in off Lake Michigan. And when we stepped from the street into the loan office, half the weather in Chicago blew right in with us. One of the girls behind the counter put on her sweater before coming over to see what we wanted.

She found out quickly enough when my partners pushed past her into the office area and forced the manager over to the safe. I was standing near the door, keeping one eye on the street and the other on the girl in the sweater. She was a little on the mousy side, hair back in a knot, fashionable-looking glasses, but with lenses thick enough to indicate that she really needed them, and not much make-up. Her features were good, though, and I think she could have been very beautiful for a man she loved enough.

The girl kept looking at the money that was going into our shopping bag, then out at the blustery street that was hubcap-deep in slush. Finally, when the bag was full, and we were almost ready to leave, she turned to me and asked, "Where will you go with all that money?"

"Oh," I said, "maybe to Brazil or Chile. Someplace like that."

126

"Mister," she said, with a sad and wistful look in her eyes, "I sure wish you could stuff me in that bag with the money and take me along."

I've often thought about that girl since, and wondered if she ever managed to free herself from the trap of that grubby little money factory. That's obviously what it was to her, just as so many other stores and businesses are traps for the people who work in them. They might spend years wearing their souls away in a place like that, accepting it as the normal and expected way of life — which, unfortunately, it is for many people. Then, one day a man comes in with a gun and, in two or three minutes, removes all of that sacred and slowly accumulated cash. For many, the man who takes that money is not just a criminal; he becomes the embodiment of an ultimate, amoral and conscienceless sort of freedom. He is someone who doesn't worry about responsibility. And, even if only for a few moments, he is someone to be envied.

This isn't only a vague and shadowy thing that I've seen in people's eyes. Time and again, I've heard it from their lips.

I was talking with a St. Louis jeweler once while I was cleaning out a few of his ring trays.

"Aren't you worried about getting caught," he asked.

"Not especially," I told him. "The street's pretty quiet, and it'll be 20 minutes yet before a police patrol comes by."

"There's a lot of money tied up in those rings. What you going to do with it?"

"Nothing much, friend. Just live well on it until it's gone."

"Then you go steal some more?"

"That's right."

"I guess you've sure got it made," he said with much ve-

127

hemence. "I just wish to hell I was in the same line of work that you are."

Reactions such as this are quite common. And if it made people feel more at ease to kvetch about business conditions, or to ask where they could find employment as holdup men, I had no objections to chatting with my victims. But that's only one type of reaction. Sometimes you can't even get a robbery victim to open his mouth. Some people are so frightened at the sight of a gun that you couldn't make them move if you stood there and shot their toes off one at a time.

On the other hand, there are a lot of idiots running around in this country — still alive, somehow — who have absolutely no respect for a gun. They get you confused with one of those jerks they read about in the Sunday supplements who go around holding up banks with water pistols. If you're not careful, they'll actually try to take your gun away from you. Sometimes, even when they know the gun is real, they will *refuse* to be robbed. I've hit places where the victims stood and screamed at me, telling me to get the hell out. Chinamen do that a lot. It's axiomatic among thieves that you should never try to rob a Chinaman. He'll call you dirty names in evil-sounding dialects. He'll throw an iron at you. He'll pretend he doesn't understand English, and he'll get down and squint up the bore of your gun to see if it needs washing and ironing. He won't give you any money.

From personal experience, I would also include Poles in that axiom. The owner of a Hamtramck grocery store once chased me for three blocks, lobbing milk bottles at me every foot of the way.

Oh, I tell you, people can be very violent. They can also be just plain nuts. Harry Zelnick came around very upset one time, because a salesgirl in a jewelry store turned out to

128

be a souvenir nut and she had swiped his hat while he was robbing the place. I'd already encountered that particular reaction. An old lady in a supermarket once asked me if she could have one of the bullets out of my revolver as a memento of the robbery. Another time, I was holding up a bar when a waitress came at me with a pair of scissors. I thought she was going to stab me, and for a couple of seconds I was in a real sweat whether to run out the door or try to frighten her back with the gun. Turned out she only wanted to snip off a piece of my handkerchief as a souvenir. Jesus God!

But people are weird that way. They like to have something that has touched violence. They are like the good ladies of Chicago who fought one another for the privilege of dipping their skirts into the blood of John Dillinger when he was shot to death in 1934. There are still many freaky sorts in the neighborhood of the old Rialto Theatre who will proudly display the bloody souvenirs of that execution. There is a woman in Los Angeles who claims to have a piece of old John's shirt. Until recently, a lock of hair purported to have been snipped from Dillinger's body, or from his dog, or some such silly thing, was on display in a restaurant in Coral Gables. And Francis Cardinal Spellman, whose private coin collection was the largest in the world, was the proud possessor of the $80 in cash removed from Dillinger's pockets at the Chicago morgue.

One of the more important aspects of armed robbery — as with a couple of other crimes I can think of — is getting away with it. If you get caught right away, you blow half the fun. And getting away with an armed robbery can usually be translated as getting away *from* an armed robbery; getting away from the scene of the crime before the

129

law can nail you in the act, or catch you with a bag of incriminating loot. What this means is that you are in tough shape if you have to go on a job alone. It's a great deal easier for two or three men to pull a robbery. They can secure the premises more quickly, they can watch each other's backs to make certain no citizen will try to play hero, and one man can wait in the car to insure the speediest possible getaway. The importance of the driver cannot be overstated.

In the more hip circles of the underworld, it is generally held that the two top drivers of all time were Juan Fangio and Clarence Heatherton. There are probably a number of uninformed race fans prepared to argue the point — with most of the disagreement centered on Clarence — but it's true all the same. You just have to judge by different standards, since Clarence made his reputation driving getaway on bank heists.

Clarence was a Londoner, and he looked every bit of it. When I first met him in Detroit, he was a spry wisp of a man, done up in baggy tweeds and wearing a pair of those steel-rimmed spectacles of the sort you see only on Englishmen and characters in old Charlie Chan movies. He also sported a toothbrush mustache that gave him a half-raffish air; like a teapot in an op-art cozy. Clarence had driven in British races and rallies for years before he was tempted into crime by a yen for an expensive Bugatti. After his first go at it, which cost him a stretch in Wormwood Scrubbs, he became a full-time wheelman and never went back to proper racing. Clarence was one of the oddballs who really liked the excitement of his work, but he always insisted that he drove only for love of that elusive Bugatti — or, as time went by, perhaps a 1,750-cc. Alfa-Romeo or a 300 SL Mercedes.

130

Clarence was as efficient as a computer behind the wheel, even though he nursed a quaint set of prejudices about cars. For instance, he never got over grousing about the disappearance of the running board, a very useful feature back in the 20's, when he started in the business. A standard technique on bank jobs in those days was to herd an assortment of cashiers and customers out to the getaway car and go tearing off with them stacked on the running boards. This show of togetherness usually kept the police from doing any careless shooting.

Another of Clarence's dislikes was the automatic transmission. I remember one occasion when we were parked outside a factory payroll office, right in the middle of a job, and the old geezer decided to give us a lecture on the subject. He concluded it — after we had pulled away amidst a clanging din of alarm bells and shouts for help — with the determinedly pious observation that automatics were wicked. "An automobile," he declared, "should have a stick shift, as God intended."

In the early days of the profession, when Clarence was starting out on his career, there were plenty of running boards and many more makes of cars to choose from than there are today. The main considerations were size and horsepower, and knowing old-timers still talk of the early Locomobiles, some models of which boasted up to 120 h.p. There were the indestructible Cadillacs, and the heavy, high-riding Buicks. Also popular for their speed all through the 30's were such makes as Hudson, Terraplane, and Essex.

Probably the most fondly remembered car among old wheelmen is the Cord. It was hard to come by, but much esteemed by the cognoscenti, because it was a remarkably nimble automobile, and because driving it demanded a certain deft touch which helped to weed out the amateurs.

131

I witnessed a classic example of such weeding on a dirt road outside Rochester, Michigan, a few years back. A few associates and I had come into possession of a Cord — a beautiful 1938 model, complete with supercharger — that had been stolen from a Grosse Pointe collector by a character who actually intended trying to sell it to a used-car lot. Normally, we wouldn't have used a car like that. It was too hot and too conspicuous, but the job was practically out in the country, and we were all just a bunch of sentimental slobs at heart. We *wanted* to use the Cord. And that made it a real disappointment when we learned that the cops had our prospective heist staked out thicker than the creekbed at Sutter's Mill.

With the job washed out, we couldn't afford to hold on to the Cord, but instead of just ditching it, we decided to let a jerk named Roger Sullivan try his luck at driving over what would have been our getaway route. Nobody liked Sully because he was always bungling things. If you conceded that man sprang from the ape, you could only conclude that Sully had tripped in mid-spring — probably getting somebody else arrested in the process. When we were blowing safes, Sully was always bumping into the guy who was carrying the nitroglycerin. When we were pulling robberies, he used to wander around exposing his ugly face to more eyewitnesses than was necessary. A couple of times, he had clumsily discharged a shotgun in our getaway car. And, even though he had had his driver's license revoked five times by the Secretary of State, he always insisted that the rest of us were a bunch of incompetents, and that he was the only one qualified to drive on a job.

These things we could have put up with, but Sully had a little flaw in his character that really got under our skins; no matter how badly he screwed things up, it was always

132

somebody else's fault. He even accused us of queering his shotgun. We kept him around in spite of all this, mostly out of consideration for his brother, a big man in narcotics with a well-earned reputation for family loyalty and extreme violence. But that didn't keep us from looking forward with much anticipation to Sully's debut as a driver.

The route he was to take was a five-mile stretch of bad curves with a 90-degree turn just before hitting the main highway. The idea was to cover the road in four minutes, which, according to our original plan, would have been the maximum allowable time to keep from being bottled up by the law. I had gone over it a half dozen times and was able to make it in three-and-one-half minutes. Sully figured he could make it in three flat.

Following at a leisurely pace in another car, we watched Sully clear the first two curves like a pro. Then he hit a quarter-mile straightaway that let him get up more speed than his sloppy reflexes could handle in a sensitive machine such as the one he was driving. He was in real trouble as soon as the road began kinking up again. He slid sideways through a left turn, pulling out considerable roadside foliage. Somehow, he got himself straightened around after heading into the next turn backwards, but that was all of it for him. Coming out of the turn, he tore through a rail fence, narrowly missed a herd of cows, and all but demolished the biggest chestnut tree in Michigan.

To our great regret, Sully didn't total himself out with the Cord — and he didn't learn anything either. He climbed out of the wreckage, glared at it as though it had just ratted him off to the cops, and snorted, "Touchy son-of-a-bitch, ain't it!"

By contrast, most cars on the road today make pretty crummy getaway vehicles. They are sprung and shocked for a nice, spongy ride, which is comfortable only when you don't have a cruiser on your tail. So wheelmen look for specific characteristics when selecting a car for a job. The first thing they want is a good stiff suspension that will cut down the lean on fast turns. And if they can swipe a model with disc brakes and antiroll bars, all the better.

The ideal getaway car, under present-day conditions, would seem to be something like a Jaguar — fast, plenty of pickup, and easy to handle in our heavy traffic. A flat cinch to outrun anything the law might have. Unfortunately, a Jaguar is *not* the ideal getaway car. I used one a couple of years ago on a holdup, and if you've never tried making it through the door of a Jaguar at a dead run with a sawed-off and a sack of money clutched to your bosom, you just don't know the meaning of limited headroom.

Important as the right car is to a getaway, though, nothing is more important than the man at the wheel. And at this, as I say, Clarence Heatherton was king. I like to think that Clarence passed at least a part of his great skill on to me when he introduced me to the art of successful armed robbery and taught me the rudiments of git-driving. Not that I've ever had any illusions about my skill as a wheelman. The truly good drivers are specialists, and very often they are men with a legitimate racing background. I don't claim that race drivers are any more given to larceny than, say jai alai players or pole vaulters, but there is a flaky fringe around the sport. When a driver does turn to crime, he's more likely to stay behind the wheel than to take up confidence schemes or the picking of pockets.

I worked with a lot of these speedway drop-outs over the years, and they are the most offbeat group of characters you could ever hope to get arrested with. There was a wheelman in Detroit, for instance, who twitched. I mean he twitched *all* the time. He had nerve spasms in his fingers and his left eyelid fluttered perpetually, like the shutter of a 16mm. Bell & Howell. It didn't seem to hang him up on his driving, but he had been barred for life from racing when it began to interfere with other drivers who developed sympathetic tics.

Another specimen was a big German, who still, somehow or other, finds occasional employment on heists around Cleveland. He looks like Charles de Gaulle, and once worked as a pit man for the great Fangio — for about two hours. He was a perfect driver for holdups — if you could keep him away from the engine. But if he so much as tweaked a spark plug, the whole motor was good for a three-week layup.

A good git-man must have a knack for coaxing total performance out of middling machines. He has to be careful and deliberate, and it doesn't hurt if he's a little paranoid. The best wheelman in St. Louis right now, as a matter of fact, is a guy who quit racing when he became convinced that the rest of the drivers on the circuit were conspiring to put him through a rail. On a heist he is always certain that every stop sign, traffic light, and speed limit is there just to trap him. He imagines prowl cars lurking in each alley, and he has this nutty idea that all women drivers are police molls. Working with this guy is harder on the nerves than a three-month stretch in solitary — but, man, is he ever careful.

The real wheel talent shows up less in aberrations than it does in proper cornering. On city streets, it's impossible to cut down approach-and-exit angles, and in order not to lose speed, the driver must have enough finesse to handle a power skid.

One of the oldest tricks in the profession is to let the cops get right on your tail on a gravel road, then suddenly swing

135

the wheel hard over for a controlled, four-wheel slide, timed to dig out onto a side road. Any wheelman who can't do this with his eyes shut would be better off in a nice, comfortable cell.

The variation on this — the 180-degree skid — requires pure genius. The only wheelman I ever knew who was really accomplished at this was a skinny, six-foot hillbilly named Beauregard Washburn, who didn't look competent to drive a swift herd of pigs. Beau had learned to skid a car through 180 degrees, with the help of a heavy load of moonshine in the rear end, down around Nashville while playing tag with the revenue agents. The night he demonstrated the trick for me, we had a 500-pound safe in the trunk and a 3,000-pound police car on our tail trying to climb right inside with the safe. We were heading east out of Kalamazoo, on a mangy little dirt road, and things looked a lot better for the cops than they did for us. But suddenly Beau tromped on the brakes and spun the wheel over. We must have done a quarter of a mile sideways and then backwards, with those police headlights getting bigger and brighter in our windshield every inch of the way. I like to died. If blood were a more subdued color, the casual observer might have thought I was bleeding to death. Finally, Beau dredged up enough power to get us moving forward again, and we were out of it. We were heading west and the cops were still barreling off to the east, presumably just as unglued as I was.

Occasionally a driver like Beauregard, with no background of legitimate racing, will make the grade as a top git-man. But professional criminals prefer professional drivers, since washouts are generally disasters. Some friends of mine learned this the hard way, when they decided to make a driver out of an ex-bookie named Howie. They taught him everything they could, and even packed him off to a school in California where they train race drivers. But Howie had neither the brains nor the coordination for driving. On his very first job he let a diagonal-parking arrangement at a small-town supermarket heist rattle him to shreds. He positioned the car in the slot backward, a technique made popular about that time by an ex-roadracer who used a convertible and worked by himself, taking advantage of the diagonal parking for a Le Mans start. But it didn't work for Howie. When his pals came piling into the car with the loot, he immediately laid down a quarter inch of rubber screaming out of that slot — *backward,* through the market's plate glass window, and right into a soap display.

The guys were lucky on that one. Even though they took part of a check-out counter with them, they were able to make it back through the window and escape in a blizzard of Ivory Flakes. But on the very next job, Howie contrived to get everybody pinched. The boys came busting out of a Detroit jewelry store, with guns and hot necklaces hanging out of every pocket, only to find that Howie had carefully wedged the car into a parking space. He wasn't even behind the wheel, for all the good it would have done. He was, God preserve us, feeding coins into the meter.

And that's the sort of thing that is becoming more and more typical of the business. The real trouble is that there aren't enough men with racing experience coming into the profession — men like my old friend Clarence. I have a fond picture in my mind of Clarence today, a little older and with thicker lenses in his glasses, but still natty in tweeds and proper English to his larcenous core. He's sitting in a freshly stolen GT 350 Mustang, immediately in front of a bank in some small eastern community — one of those quiet places off the main highway with miles of country road stretching out in all directions. Clarence has one eye cocked on the

137

town constable, and the other on his confederates in the bank (common criminals, of whom he doesn't really approve), but his mind is on that fine power plant in front of him, listening to it tick over, and just waiting to let it out on the only kind of race that ever mattered to him.

That's not too unlikely a vision, though it's coming to be a very rare one. The one-time specialty of git-driving is losing its color, I'm afraid, and is being taken over by dolts who pull jobs on the spur of the moment and drive off, willy-nilly, into the back bumpers of police cars, or get hung up at toll booths with nothing smaller than a hot 20. It's enough to take the heart right out of you.

And things aren't much better for armed robbers in general. It's reached the point where there are even holdup men like Tony Wells, who, so far as I know, is still at large. Tony is what you could call a wee bit dim, both in wit and in vision. The lenses of his glasses are fully a quarter-of-an-inch thick. There is a greenish cast to them, and even from straight in front they look like an infinity of concentric rings with piggy little pupils of bull's-eyes right in the center. He has an unpleasant habit of easing up on you while you are talking with him, until finally he is squinting myopically at the pores in your nose from a distance of only two or three inches. And, even if you've known him for many years, you always get the feeling that this intense scrutiny never quite results in recognition. For Tony, the gap between microcosm of pores and the macrocosm of person is an unrealized and impassable abyss.

The entire tone of Tony's career is best illustrated by the boner he pulled when he and a couple other guys decided to heist a bail bondsman directly across the street from the Beaubien precinct station. This, in itself, was none too cool, but Tony wasted no time in making it worse. As soon as the

138

car pulled up to the curb, he hopped out, cheerily calling back to his confederates:

"Keep the engine running, boys. I'll show you how to take off a score the way it's supposed to be done."

This in a voice that must have rattled windows clear out to Dearborn. Then, with determination shining brightly through his lenses, and a huge pistol clutched conspicuously in his right hand, he swaggered off across the street — right towards the station house.

If Tony's confederates hadn't been able to tackle him at the top of the station steps, he would surely have gone right the hell ahead, and stuck up the desk sergeant.

Just once I got roped into working with this dingbat, and that wouldn't have happened if I'd known beforehand that he was going to be along. But good old Harry Zelnick called me up one day and said that he and two other guys were going to take off a savings-and-loan office. He wanted me along for the fourth man, because we could only be inside for two minutes. It would take at least four of us to clean the joint out. So, what the heck; I'd known Harry for a long time, and he didn't figure to be working with any idiots — especially when he had the obvious good sense to invite a steady hand like mine along. Since I couldn't help but admire his judgement, I told him to count me in.

When Harry drove around to pick me up, I saw he had Tony in the car, along with another guy I'd never seen before. I wasn't worried about the new guy, because he couldn't have been any worse than Tony even if he'd been the new Police Commissioner.

"Harry," I said, leaning down to the car window, "My brother just turned up pregnant and I don't think I can make it."

"Now, wait a minute, pal. You gotta come along. The job

139

has to be this afternoon and it's too late to get anyone else."

I was already committed and I knew it, but I had to be in a position where I could at least say "I told you so" when they were strapping us in the chair.

"Friend Harry, I would rather go on a job with Dick Tracy than with this idiot. Why don't we just drive down and turn ourselves in and get it over with?"

"He ain't gonna do nothin' but keep time," Harry promised. "So help me. We march him in and we march him out. Now, get in and let's get started."

Against my better judgement, I got in and Harry drove the four of us out to Birmingham where the savings and loan was located. Tony whistled *Poor Butterfly* all the way out.

When we got to the score, Harry parked the car directly across the street and gave Tony some last minute coaching.

"Look," he told him, "all you gotta do is keep an eye on your watch. As soon as two minutes is up, you yell and we all split back to the car. You got it straight?"

Tony squinted at him. "Got no watch," he said.

"Well, for chrissake, here! Use mine."

Harry handed his watch to Tony.

"Now, can you read the damn thing?"

Tony put the watch on and held his wrist two inches in front of his face.

"Yuh," he said.

I don't think any of us really had much hope for the deal at that point, but we got out of the car and went across the street to the office.

Things seemed to go a little better when we got inside and pulled out our guns. No one panicked. The few customers and employees behaved like model victims, obeying orders and standing quietly. Tony stationed himself against

140

the wall opposite the money cages. Harry and the other guy
— I never did find out his name — went behind the counter for the big stuff while I started working my way along
the windows, picking up the money from the drawers.

I'd worked my way through about half the windows when
I decided I'd better check on Tony. I turned around and he
had his gun pointed straight at me.

"Get them hands up," he said.

One of the young ladies behind the counter giggled, and
I blushed. I had never felt so unprofessional in my life.

"Tony," I said, as calmly as I could, "don't pull the damn
trigger."

I moved over to one side and approached him outside his
line of fire. Taking him by the shoulders, I turned him 90
degrees to the right and lined his gun up on a coat rack
twenty feet down the wall.

"Now, keep that guy covered," I said. "If he moves an
inch, you shoot hell out of him."

The secretary giggled again. I almost felt like giggling
my own damn self.

I left Tony guarding the coat rack and went back to the
windows. He still had the wrist with the watch on it up by
his eyes. His hand was cocked palm-out away from his forehead. He looked like the heroine from an old silent movie
— the one who was always saying in the subscripts, "Oh, if
you have tears, prepare to shed them now."

I hadn't been thinking about the time, but as I was scoop-
ing out the next to the last drawer I heard Harry yelling:

"Hey, Tony! How the hell long we been?"

"Dunno," said Tony. "What time we come in?"

Without a word of consultation or a second of delay, the
three of us who were capable of thought headed for the
door. I would have been happy to leave Tony behind to

141

shoot it out with the coat rack, but Harry snatched him by the collar, and we ran for the car.

That was the last job I ever pulled in Detroit; almost the last job I ever pulled anyplace. No sooner had Harry pulled out into the stream of traffic than four police cars converged on the loan office. It was *that* close. And that was *too* close.

Very clearly, it was time for me to get the hell out of Michigan.

CHAPTER TWELVE

Jewel robberies always fascinated me, even though I was forced to work under a severe handicap. It grieves me to admit it, but I can't tell the difference between a 50-cent string of glass beads and a $50,000 choker of diamonds. There is apparently some subtle thing about precious stones that escapes me. A green stone could be anything from an emerald to an old beer bottle, and the possibilities for the colorless sparklers are endless. But there is an irresistible glamor about jewel theft, an aura of villas on the Riviera, yachts, luxury hotels, Grace Kelly, Interpol, THE CAT BURGLAR STRIKES AGAIN, smooth-throated women, and I'll meet you in Istanbul.

I was generally successful in overcoming my handicap by estimating the quality of my victim, rather than the quality of the gems. My first jewel score was a diamond pendant belonging to a maiden lady friend of Milly's out in San Francisco. She was a sweet old soul who couldn't abide imitations or anything cheap and tawdry. I judged, and I judged correctly, that a woman of her tastes would not hang me up with a piece of paste. And the loss of her pendant was only justice, since she had made it eminently clear on a number of occasions that she couldn't abide *me*.

Much of my subsequent jewel work was done on the East Coast — most of it in such suburban wastelands as Darien and Westchester County. A far cry from the Riviera that was; a blighted countryside of septic tank salesmen and pothead babysitters. The money was there, though. Babbitt, baby, hang on to your wallet.

But I wasn't even thinking of jewel heists when I left Detroit. I only wanted to get as far as I could from old faces and old cells. And I wanted to do it without getting another dose of California. So, with no more purpose than an inclination to the east, I headed for New York.

All I can say for New York is that it's not a very respectable city. Consider the laws of probability, if you will. A stranger moving to Detroit and taking a room in a randomly chosen apartment house would almost certainly find himself living with a lot of Ford Motor assembly-line workers. They'd have their beer on weekends, and they might get a little boisterous now and then. But they would be, on the whole, perfectly square, honest, and dull citizens. You would have to shop around for quite a while before you found anything that might pass for a den of thieves. Not so in New York.

Whether it was due to a breach in the system of averages, or to a mystical affinity for thieves that somehow attached itself to me at an early stage of my development, the apartment that I rented in East Harlem turned out to be in a building where the hustlers outnumbered the cockroaches. In the apartment adjacent to mine there lived a gentleman who left the building every evening carrying a heavy satchel.

144

The clasp came loose one evening, and I was rewarded with a look at the contents. Burglar tools. I'd handled them often enough to know, and there was no mistaking them. This fellow was a crook. And, in one form or another, so were all the other tenants. The crabby old man on the second floor — a specialist at beating the change machines in laundromats. Those two hip-looking girls on the third floor — hookers with $50-a-day habits. There was a motherly old babe who was pushing marijuana, a fag who was doing something questionable with traveler's checks, and a college type who was boosting loose items from parked cars. Thrown in with that bunch, I almost felt like a virgin.

The one island of honesty in this sea of larceny seemed to be a sculptor who had a studio on the top floor. And his apparent honesty was so out of place in that abode that his presence there was somehow jarring — until I found out what his hustle really was.

As a sculptor, Herbert d'Amboise did remarkably good work. His studio was a veritable ceramic jungle of half-finished busts, daintily posturing nudes, and mythological figures frozen in perpetual embrace with mortal wenches. Some of the pieces in this latter category were so frankly carnal that it would have been difficult to imagine them on display anywhere, but at least one of them had enjoyed temporary prominence in Central Park.

This came about a few years earlier, when Herbert created a mighty portrayal of Europa holding beastly congress with Zeus as he was working out of his bull bag. It was exact in every detail, and as Herbert gazed upon it, he realized with a sinking heart that it would very probably never be shown in Rockefeller Center or purchased for the adornment of any Post Office steps. The public would be deprived of enlightenment and Herbert would be deprived of his

145

glory. In the midst of his depression, Herbert was smitten with inspiration; he would forcibly bring culture to the peasants.

Enlisting the aid of a fellow sculptor, Herbert transported his statue to Central Park and mounted the already mounted Europa in a conspicuous location next to the main drive. Then he and his accomplice made themselves comfortable on a park bench to await the revealing light of dawn.

By actual count, the statue was enjoyed, gawped at, abhorred, execrated, drooled over, and otherwise noticed by more than 400 New Yorkers before a Parks Commission truck and five policemen showed up at noon. They modestly wrapped the offending creation in a tarpaulin and hauled it away to an unknown fate, though Herbert suspects to this day that it was kept by the Commissioner of Parks or by a high-ranking police official — and for reasons more lascivious than artistic.

The biggest agony in Herbert's life was the very widespread failure of the public to appreciate his worth as an artist. During a good month, he might manage to sell two or three small figurines. These didn't even cover the expense of clay, plaster, and armature wire, not to mention rent, food, incidental bills, and the fees for the models he sometimes employed. He didn't really seem to care about the money, but the lack of interest in his work galled him beyond endurance.

"Those pigs!" he would scream, referring to the two modernist sculptors who owned studios in the building across the street. "Junk they make. Machinery they weld together. Abortions of sewing machines. Eggs with holes in them. I was over there last week, and one of these offal-eating cretins was welding a woman with old sprockets and motor mountings from an Allis-Chalmers tractor. For breasts he was using fuel pumps. Who would sleep with a coffee grinder, I ask you? Am I eating eggs with steel pimples? But these pigs, they are getting rich selling brazen vomit to idiots. And I am starving to death."

The funny part of it was that Herbert was a long way from starving to death. He was always sending out to the delicatessen for hot pastrami and turkey sandwiches, and he consumed prodigious quantities of reasonably good liquor. It was also rumored that he was paying his models for services less passive than posing. This paradox of no income and a comfortable standard of living looked suspiciously familiar to me, so I took the direct approach and asked him what his hustle was. He told me.

Herbert was supplementing his income by selling Van Gogh's ear. This isn't the sort of thing you can sell to just anybody. He found his customers in the wealthier elements of the off-Broadway theatre crowd, and among the patrons of art galleries and private showings. The ears were skillfully sculptured in chipped beef — baked to a suitably wizened condition — and mounted on red velvet in wooden boxes with hermetically sealed glass lids. Burned into the bottom of each box were the words, MUSÉE DES IMPRESSIONNISTES — ARLES, strongly hinting at a museum theft.

With immense pride, Herbert showed me one of his ears. It was good enough to fool another ear any day of the week.

"You will notice," he explained, "that this is a left ear. My customers are all snobs who have seen Van Gogh's self-portrait showing the right side of his head bandaged. They always jump on me as though, Aha, they've caught me with an ear that someone has cut from the wrong side of a drunken derelict. Then I tell them how Van Gogh did the painting from a mirror, and that gets them every time."

147

Herbert was averaging two or three sales a month with his phony ears, and he was getting $100 apiece for them. If any of his customers ever tumbled to the deception, they never complained; probably out of fear that they'd be drummed from the ranks of the avant-garde if word got around.

Only once did Herbert miss out on a sale. A notoriously tight-fisted Broadway producer wanted that ear in the worst sort of way. He was practically begging for the thing, but after an hour of haggling he still couldn't find it in his penurious heart to offer more than ten dollars for it. Herbert was so furious at this double insult, both to himself and his craftsmanship and to the memory of Van Gogh, that he smashed in the lid of the box and, right before the startled eyes of his customer, ate the ear.

Another lurker-in-the-corners of this apartment building was a man named Al. And it was Al who finally got me to thinking seriously about jewel theft.

Al was a fairly ordinary looking guy, who was always smiling — but who still managed, somehow, to seem thoroughly sinister, like a real skull passing for a Halloween pumpkin. We talked with each other frequently, during my first few weeks in the building, and, as each of us came to realize — through small remarks that were let drop — that the other must have spent a lot of time in prison, we became pretty good friends. Eventually, we were openly discussing our prison experiences. From that, it was only a short step to cutting up current scores, and a hairbreadth away from criminal conspiracy.

A major advantage to jewel theft, as Al outlined it to me, is that you always know who your victims are. If they are wealthy enough to have jewels worth stealing, they are also prominent enough to have their comings and goings

148

thoroughly publicized. By casing his jobs in the society pages, watching the television shows that feature visiting notables, reading *Variety,* and gagging his way through a treacly morass of gossip columns, the jewel thief can acquaint himself with who is staying in what hotel, and which pendants are being worn by whom.

This is the handy sort of information that made it possible for a couple of friends of mine to walk off with $400,000 in jewels belonging to the wife of Hollywood producer David O. Selznick. And it was also a gossip-column tip that told the same two thieves exactly when Mrs. Jack Benny would be absent from her hotel suite. They relieved her of $200,000. The list of the rich and famous who have been similarly deprived of their baubles after a revealing shot of publicity would read like a Tiffany mailing list: Janet Leigh, Doris Duke, Barbara Hutton, Marlene Dietrich, Eva Gabor, Grace Kelly, the McGuire sisters, Mrs. Edward G. Robinson, pop singer Connie Francis, and Mursie Malachok. I don't know who the hell Mursie is, but a friend of mine saw her on a television show one night while he was sitting in a Manhattan bar with no place to go and nothing to steal. She looked wealthy, and when she mentioned the hotel where she was staying my friend beat it over there and clipped her for $12,000 worth of diamonds. He made it back to the bar in time to see the end of the show.

When you see a theft such as this written up in the newspapers, you get the impression that it was a daring and brilliantly conceived job, probably the work of a master criminal. This is because the men who write the newspaper stories, despite their professional cynicism, are greatly overstimulated by the glamor of a good jewel heist: the cat burglar mystique at work again. And add to this a dollar loss that has been thoroughly inflated for the benefit of the

149

insurance company, and the name of a celebrity or society victim, and you have a news story that usually rates space on the front page.

To see a job like that in its true perspective, try visualizing the same circumstances with different principals. Instead of the victim being a movie star, and the loot an emerald tiara, imagine the same apartment occupied by a garter salesman named Lester Pelton. The loot, in Lester's case, will be a knockwurst sandwich in the upper right-hand drawer of his dresser. To steal that knockwurst, our jewel thief takes the elevator up to Lester's floor, slips the lock on the door with a strip of Celluloid — or even with one of the hotel's laminated DO NOT DISTURB signs — and he's home free.

Does the press play up the diabolical cleverness of this score? Does Lester hold a press conference in the lobby? Is there a hue and cry for that purloined knockwurst? In a pig's valise there is.

Well, the star's tiara would demand a lot less daring and brilliance. Not only is it easier to pinpoint her hotel and her room, and to find out that she's not going to be home, there is also an excellent chance that she doesn't even bother locking her door. Jewels carry much more insurance than knockwurst, and the people who own them are notoriously careless about protecting them. There have even been crass suggestions to the effect that celebrities are not adverse to the publicity that attends a heist. In any case, they almost always keep their ice in the same upper right-hand drawer that served Lester so inadequately.

Al was a very good thief, and we functioned smoothly together on the five or six hotel jobs that we pulled. We also did pretty well on a like number of residential burglaries. Al was a master at entering a building without making an undue amount of noise, and he was generally considerate enough not to step in people's prize hydrangeas, or trample down their box hedges, while looking for the best point at which to break in. But I was relatively inexperienced at this, and Al did, after all, have his flaws. Consequently, there were some jobs that didn't exactly go off like clockwork.

So long as we were performing our second-story work on empty residences, I managed to handle myself in a very proper, thief-like manner. But my romantic streak, the impractical and impressionable side of me that has caused things to go wrong more than once, came to the fore most inopportunely the first time we found ourselves in an occupied dwelling.

Up to a point, the job went perfectly. Our score was a fine old home in Westchester, not far from the headquarters of the unsmokable *Reader's Digest*. The jewel stash in the bedroom safe had been fingered for us by an ex-convict electrician who had done some wiring in the house. And we had it from the pen of no less a personage than Dorothy Kilgallen that the owners would be attending a wedding reception in the city that night.

Al found an extension ladder in the garage and, together, we lugged it around the house, counting windows until we located the ones that would give access to the master bedroom. We propped the ladder against the wall and climbed up to the window. As is so often the case with second-floor windows, it was unlocked.

Once inside, Al pulled the shades. Then, since the only windows in the room looked out over an expanse of lawn and woods and were not visible to any neighbors, he turned on the lights.

We weren't alone. There was a bed against the far wall,

opposite the windows, and there was a woman in it. As soon as the lights came on, she sat up and blinked at us.

I knew from past experience with armed robbery that it's highly important to keep the victims relaxed and to soothe their fears. You can't expect to have things go off safely and smoothly when people are running around in a panic, begging for their lives, screaming for the cops, or trying to take your gun away from you. Since this was not an armed robbery, however, I really wasn't looking for anything like a panic reaction. Though if there were one, I felt more than competent to handle it. All it required was a calm reassurance and a display of gentility. That's how Arthur Barry always handled it.

Barry, probably the greatest jewel thief in the history of crime, had stolen more than $10,000,000 worth of gems. And most of it had come from the expensive homes in Westchester County, Long Island, Newport, and Kings Point. Forty years earlier, and only a few short miles from where Al and I were pulling our heist, the gentleman cat burglar and an accomplice had lifted $100,000 in jewels from the *enfant terrible* of Wall Street, Jesse Livermore.

Barry's impeccable behavior in the Livermore boudoir had been splashed across every front page in the country. And the beautiful, 18-year-old Mrs. Livermore's account of his solicitous behavior had set to fluttering the heart of every bejeweled dowager within 50 miles of Kings Point. Not only had Barry declined to deprive her of $4,000 in pin money, he had gone so far as to sort her favorite baubles from the loot and press them back into her hand before taking his jaunty leave through the bedroom window.

That sort of gallantry wasn't merely a gesture with Barry. It was typical of his character. Back in Michigan, I had served time with a man who had known Barry in Dannemora, many years before. According to him, Barry's favorite maxim of criminal success had been: "Always show courtesy — to the victim and, most especially, to the police. Courtesy is the virtue of a gentleman, and no sweet woman has ever panicked in the face of it. Courtesy will save you countless inconveniences, not to mention innumerable pinches."

Those words of wisdom, coming secondhand as they did from the old master, had graven themselves indelibly upon my little mind. From that time forward, it had been my conceit that I could not only outdo the suavity of Arthur Barry — who, after all, had sprung from a poor Irish background — but that one day I might even outmatch in *politesse* the original Raffles. And now, at last, I had my chance.

I could see that the woman whose room we had invaded was certainly no 18-year-old society belle, as had been Arthur Barry's Mrs. Livermore. In fact, she was on the puffy side of 50 and heavily inclined toward frowziness. I was rather disappointed not to find even a small suggestion of glamor in our lumpy victim. Still, she was a woman alone, a member of the well-heeled gentry, and a sensitive human creature who deserved to be treated with a full measure of respect. I felt a great sympathy for her as she sat alone on that huge bed, fear blossoming in her pig-like little eyes at the spectacle of two strange men in her room. Clearly a Barryesque touch of charm was in order.

"Don't be afraid, Madame," said I, with all the suavity of a master jewel thief, "we're only after your jewelry, and I can assure you that neither of us will harm you."

"My jewels?" she croaked, still half asleep and only half comprehending.

"Yes, Ma'am. Only the jewels." I motioned toward her

153

nightstand where two decanters were labeled "scotch" and "rye." "Would you care for a drink to settle your nerves until we leave?"

Now she was awake.

"Whaddya talkin' about, you bum? Yer stealin' my damn jewels and ya wanna feed me my own damn liquor? That's a hell of a note! Just get yer ass outta my Goddamn house is all I want you should do."

"Madame," I said, much taken aback at her rudeness, "please control yourself and try to make a bit less noise. Think of the neighbors."

"The neighbors! Screw the Goddamn neighbors," she screamed. "You got a helluva nerve comin' in here this time of night wakin' people up an' offerin' them their own Goddamn whiskey. I'll give *you* whiskey, you crook!"

So saying, she seized up one of the cut-glass decanters and leaped from the bed, menacing me with the scotch.

At this point, Al intervened. "Alright, you dizzy bitch," he said, "shaddup and siddown or I'll belt ya one in the kisser."

Apparently she found Al's gruff words of reassurance comforting, as she sat down immediately and didn't offer another word during the remainder of the robbery.

It was on this same job that Al and I also set some sort of a record by losing our getaway car. We had stolen it in the first place, so the loss wasn't serious, financially speaking. It just made a shambles of our getaway. There we were, wandering around in the wilds of Westchester, with our pockets full of loot, and neither of us could figure out where we'd parked the car. So we split up, each taking a different side road and agreeing to meet at a street light we could see nearly half a mile away. If we hadn't found the car by then we would have to hike back to civilization.

154

When I came dragging up to the street light half an hour later it was to be greeted with a sight that chilled my ruddy blood. Enough to make your cullions crawl, it was. Al had gotten there ahead of me. Beneath a huge oak tree across the road there was a curbside phone booth. Al had his pistol aimed through the accordion doors and, even as I stood aghast, he fired. All I could think of were the countless Hollywood thrillers I'd seen as a kid. Everybody knows what happens to people in phone booths. Al was killing somebody in there! As though goosed by an unseen hand, I flew across the road.

"Al, don't do it!" I screamed. "They'll give us both the chair!"

I landed on Al's back and the gun went off again. Everything went black. I didn't know if Al had shot me, or if I'd caught a slug from the ungrateful wretch in the phone booth.

Things came back into focus a moment later with the light of Al's cursing. The shot had struck the street light, but Al made it very plain, as he groped about on hands and knees, that the next Goddamn shot was all mine — if he could find his son-of-a-bitching gun and get me in the frigging sights.

It was a full week before he would even explain that he had been trying to shoot the coin box off the phone in order to get enough small change to call a cab for our getaway.

It had never occurred to me that Al might be trying to shoot a lock open. I hadn't been stealing half as long as Al, and I'd been cured of the shot-lock mystique years ago. Like so many others, I had been a victim of one of the most dangerous Celluloid myths ever to dribble out of Hollywood. I can't even begin to count the number of pictures I saw as a kid where the villain orders the stage driver to throw down the strong box — then, instead of asking the driver for the Goddamn key, he takes his Colt .45 and blows the lock off. I have even seen actors do this while holding the strong box in their lap.

Fortunately, I wasn't remembering anything that extreme on the one occasion when I tried using a gun for a key. By some saving grace, I had in mind the movie detective who charges up to a locked door and screams, "Stand back everybody! I'm gonna shoot the lock."

The lock I shot was on the rear entrance to an automotive parts warehouse in Detroit. I stood back a cautious six feet, took careful aim with a .45 automatic, turned my head away and pulled the trigger. That lock, let me tell you, was barely scarred. But it took a doctor two weeks to pick up all the ricocheted fragments of that bullet out of my arm and cheek.

I worked with Al, off and on, for two years. I stood a couple of pinches — for minor transgressions that had nothing to do with our partnership — but, aside from that, the hustling was good and the relationship was excellent. Things were so good in New York, in fact, that I might still be there and have two or three fewer prison raps to my credit if I hadn't happened to run into an old friend.

It was one of those encounters that happen so often in life; the sort that comes to nothing in itself, but that exercises just enough force on you to send your life caromming off on a new tangent. For me, a new tangent has usually meant getting locked up.

This time, I found my tangent on 42nd Street. I was heading for a little bar I knew, thinking about the next sting that Al and I had lined up, when I found myself taking more than a casual interest in a woman walking ahead of me. She was long and lithe and lovely, a firm-bodied woman, and I was attracted first by the subtle play of the muscles in her calves as she strode along. Then I noticed her hair. There was something distinctly familiar in its tawny tone, and in the way it hung clear down to her can. Even before I caught up with her and got a look at her face, I knew it could only be Marlene Regis, my kinky friend from Detroit.

Marlene was as happy as I was to see a friendly face from the old days. She was so happy about it, so buoyantly overjoyed to see me, that I couldn't find it in my heart to deny her my company in bed that night. She was also, as it turned out, looking for someone to help her with a check-passing scheme she had in mind. Would I like to go along for the ride? You bet. As tangents go, Marlene was a hell of a lot more entertaining than Al.

CHAPTER THIRTEEN

There is an old-time hoodlum-turned-pub-keeper in Chicago who, as a matter of record, once took a race horse for a "ride" after it had cost him a small fortune with the bookies. There is also a story current among his friends that he was once contracted by the syndicate for a special rub-out job.

"We'll give you ten grand for this hit," the mob's representatives told him.

"Ten G's!" he said. "How come so much? I never get more'n five."

"This," they explained, "will be a tough hit for you. We wanna give you a little something extra."

"G'wan, there ain't no tough hits and I got my ethics. Just gimme the five."

"We're tellin' you it's a rough job," they said. "The guy we want dumped is Lippy Pask."

"Lippy! That's a pal o' mine, for chrissake. . . . I'll do the job for nothing."

The story has a certain apocryphal ring to it. The first time I heard it was just after I had stuck this guy with a bad check. It made quite an impression on me at the time. It didn't discourage Marlene, though. She never worried about getting in trouble, or getting pinched, or catching the clap, or anything. And, so far as I know, she is still untroubled, unpinched, and just as sweet and clean and tasty as when we laid our trail of wallpaper from New York to Chicago, through Springfield and Lexington and points south.

Marlene was good with checks, and we made a beautiful team. Posing as a married couple, we stopped at all the best hotels, ate in the finest restaurants, and drank in the poshest bars. We oozed dignity and sophistication, and we hung checks every place we went. The living was good, the nights with Marlene were a delight, and the money rolled in. And, even if we spent it as fast as we got it, we were having a solid ball. But I had misgivings.

Although there is a lot of money in it, cashing checks is not an especially good way to make a dishonest dollar. The trouble is, that when they pinch you for one bad check they usually end up finding out about most of the others. So they convict you on one check and send you to prison for it. Then the other people who are holding your old wallpaper lodge detainers against you, which gives them an option to prosecute and re-imprison you in their respective venues after you've worn out your original sentence. You bounce from prison to prison, until you begin to think there is more rubber in your hindquarters than in the checks you cashed.

If a fellow has any sensitivity or foresight about him, he tends to worry about such eventualities. This is precisely the prospect I was stewing over one afternoon in a St. Louis saloon when I got to thinking about Jim Fitzpatrick. I'd known him in Jackson prison. He was an old forger who had

159

bugged out under the pressure of too many years in too many cells. When I knew him, he was serving out his time in the prison's psychiatric clinic. Getting out, for him, didn't mean much more than a transfer from the prison to a state hospital. A short trip from one cage to another, with a guaranteed lifetime daily dose of the same treatment that had sent him around the bend in the first place.

The interesting thing about Jim was the nature of his delusion. He was convinced that he had finally achieved perfection in his chosen profession. In a way, he had. Jim spent his days in the mental ward making beautiful crayon drawings of checks on sheets of toilet paper. He used different colors for different banks. The Chase Manhattan checks were a rich, substantial red. For the Bank of America, he used a monetary green. Institutions of less renown had to settle for more frivolous checks, rendered in yellow, orange, or pink. Traveler's checks, for some reason, were done in their true colors, and with superb accuracy. I've known men who cashed checks that were scrawled on the front of a bank's letterhead envelope. One guy even used to go around hanging checks drawn on the Left Bank of the Mississippi. And, having cashed many a check *stub* myself, it is no exaggeration to say that Jim's checks could undoubtedly have been cashed without too much trouble. They were that good.

Jim saved his black crayons exclusively for signing the checks. He had an interesting system for this. On Sundays, he forged all his checks in the name of Baron Rothschild. And on the days that he was subjected to therapy, he invariably made out the checks to draw on the account of the chief psychiatrist. There was a definite grudge system to his forgeries. On those days when he seemed lucid enough to realize where he was, the checks would be signed by the

160

warden or by one of the guards. He also dipped into the accounts of any of the inmate nurses who might have been slow in replenishing his crayon supply. I never did learn what he had against the Baron.

Old Jim hung his rubber works all over the ward; on doctors, on inmate nurses, and even on the other nuts. His forgeries were such works of art that everyone was more than happy to humor him. When he went through the chow line, he would give the supervising steward a toilet-paper check to cover the meal. Sometimes he paid for everybody. He did the same with the attendants who brought him fresh linen, distributing pourboires in the grand manner of a prince of the blood.

One day he bummed a cigarette from me and gave me a Chase Manhattan check for my trouble. His eyes were blandly innocent as he handed it to me, but ⸯ could hear him chuckling over his score as he walked away smoking my cigarette. He bought all his smokes the same way.

Jim's bum checks were always accepted without question. He had plenty to smoke and plenty to eat, and he never worried about a pinch. He even had the satisfaction of getting cops to cash his checks. Some place inside of himself, he was living in a check-passer's paradise. He was doing everything I was doing, only *he* wasn't worried about getting caught and *he* was happy as hell.

Marlene and I had special plans for Atlanta, Georgia. A year earlier, Marlene had been shacked up for a couple of days with a man who owned a factory there. She had relieved him of $300 as the price for her love, and she had also had the foresight to swipe a book of company checks from his suitcase.

On the way south, we had picked up a check protector,

161

and we had figured out the best way for beating the company. All we had to do was start the right machine at the
right time.

This entire country is a huge machine. And it is filled
with an endless spawn of machines — machines into which
you stuff a self-respecting pig and out comes a sausage;
machines that take individual cacao beans and blend them
into an acceptably homogeneous chocolate; machines that
convert the lovely italics of a woman's calligraphy into real
honest-to-god imitation type, with each letter micrometri-
cally identical to the rest. We have gadgets and gilhickies,
and long-spindled armatures, and things that go burp in the
night; photo-cells to check us through metered doorways,
transducers to push and shove, relays to relay, and all their
whirring, clicking kin that usher folk from one slot to the
next and regulate the wheels of commerce.

The machines are fast, and the machines are efficient.
But the machines that watch over the flow of checks maintain the same hours as their masters. And you know how it
goes with bankers.

Our plan was to have all the checks ready to go at once.
We would each take a fistful of them and cover the whole
town over a weekend. By the time the checks reached the
bank on Monday morning, and the machines began gagging
on them, Marlene and I would be baking in the sun of a
Florida beach.

We broke our pattern in Atlanta to the extent that we
took a room in a fairly crummy hotel. Here there was no
need to put up a ritzy front to hang our paper, and it was
wiser to sacrifice a bit of luxury for the sake of remaining
inconspicuous. So we checked ourselves into a fleabag. And
while Marlene went out to see a man about some phony
identification, I went to work on the checks.

162

After four hours of agonizingly careful work, I was confident that the product of my labor looked genuine enough to swamp Atlanta clear to the scuppers. I had 100 phony payroll checks dummied up, run through the check protector, and signed by the company treasurer, a fellow named Simon Snitworth. I felt a little silly forging a name like that, but when I was through, Snitworth himself would have guaranteed those checks. Marlene had even gone to the trouble of checking the plant's pay scale, and I had the paper made out to such amounts as $126.84 and $111.48. Atlanta bartenders had been cashing those company checks for years without having one bounce. For these babies, we wouldn't even need false identification.

By the time I was through with the job, our room was a fine, incriminating mess, with blank checks, inks, check protectors, rubber stamps, watermarked check paper, and finished forgeries scattered all over the place. I had just started putting things back together when there was a knock at the door.

"Who is it?" I called.

A very plausible voice on the other side said, "Bellboy."

Now, I'd seen this bit many times before in the movies, and I wouldn't have believed that voice if I'd been engaged in nothing more felonious than trimming the hairs in my nostrils. The Hollywood crook is always holed up in a town where he doesn't know a soul. He hasn't even thought of calling room service, because the hotel is too cheap to supply such amenities or because he is too busy peeking out through the Venetian blinds and propping straight back chairs against the door. Still, the first time a cop with a falsetto voice hammers on the door and yells "Bellhop," he opens up like a hippopotamus at feeding time.

I wasn't about to go for a deal like that. Very craftily, I

163

tippy-toed over to the door, got down on all fours, and peered through the crack at the bottom. I counted eight shoes on the other side of the door. They were all black, and six of them had blue serge breaking across the instep. I figured this to be a very unlikely sort of bellhop.

Getting up, I eased over to the bed and began squeaking the springs energetically. I hoped it sounded as though I were getting up and putting on my trousers.

"Hang on," I yelled. "Be right with you."

That was good for maybe five or ten seconds delay. After that, I knew, they'd kick the door slap off its hinges. I made the window in three silent, panicky strides, snatching a completed check off the dresser in mid-flight. Luckily, the window went up without a squeak.

I hit that fire escape exactly twice — once on the grating outside my window and once on the railing directly opposite as I dropped the 15 feet to the alley below. With my usual agility, I somehow contrived to land in a trash container. Bottles and tin cans went clattering off in all directions, setting up a din that would surely bring those cops into my room and straight to the open window with guns drawn. Despite the fact that my left foot was wedged into a Del Monte pear can, I rolled free of the trash container and dashed for the street. At the end of the alley I paused just long enough to pry the can from my foot, then stepped casually out onto the sidewalk. There was a cop sitting in a squad car directly in front of the hotel entrance, but he didn't even give me a glance as I mingled with the passers-by and headed downtown.

I had no idea how the law had gotten on to us so quickly, but I knew it had to have something to do with Marlene. So I put her out of my mind and concentrated on the problem of getting the hell out of Atlanta. Instinct said to head north.

164

That seemed reasonable enough, at the time, and things probably would have turned out much the same no matter what direction I'd taken. What I didn't know right then was that Marlene had gone to the fanciest beauty shop in Atlanta and tried to do a little extracurricular check passing. She had gotten herself pinched, and even though she subsequently managed to beat the rap, the cops had automatically sent out a squad to check the hotel. Now I had every cop in a four-county area looking for me.

There are a lot of cops in Georgia, and it didn't take them long to catch me. I got out of Atlanta by taking a cab to the city limits and hitchhiking from there. A farmer picked me up and quoted hog prices to me until he turned off a few miles up the highway, letting me out in front of a roadside store. It wasn't much, but it was the only place available. I went inside and cashed the one check I'd managed to salvage.

Talk about being caught flat in the act. When I came out of the store, the first thing I saw was a road patrol car with four cops in it parked across the highway. When I put up my thumb, they wheeled their car around and pulled up beside me.

"Hey, Boy!" one of them said. "Let's see some 'dentification."

As it happened, I had four separate sets of it in my pocket. That wasn't too cool in this situation.

"Got none," I said.

"Get in," he said, swinging the door open.

"Get screwed," I said, taking off toward the nearest cotton field with much haste.

I woke up with knots on my head and the sweetly acid taste of blood in my mouth. The cell was like any number of

165

others I'd seen; typical bastille decor, with bars across one end and an iron cot hinged to the wall, partly padded with an ancient, straw-stuffed mattress. Naturally, there were the usual plumbing facilities, both chipped and cracked and colorfully orange-green in the autumn of their years.

Before I tried sitting up, I carefully ran my hand over my ribs. You don't always notice a broken one immediately, and they can give you hell if you jump right up and start doing calisthenics. My quick survey indicated that all ribs were floating calmly in their accustomed places, and none seemed abnormally detached, either fore or aft. There were a number of sore points in between, but these hurt just as much when I wasn't moving as when I was, so I lumped them under miscellaneous contusions. Neither of my legs appeared to be broken either.

After a while, I sat up slowly and waited for the throbbing to subside. Then I pulled myself over to the remnants of a mirror on the wall to see how pretty I looked. My lips were cut and swollen but, so far as I could see, my teeth were still intact. There was considerable blood matted in my hair, and one of my ears looked more like a botanist's nightmare of a liverwort than the delicate, shell-like appendage it normally was. At least the ear was still attached to my head, and that much-abused part of me seemed to have held up a shade better than Humpty-Dumpty. Overlaying a moon-shaped welt on my forehead was a dark and similarly shaped smudge. There seemed to be a series of strange markings across the center of the smudge. Leaning closer to the mirror, I pried open my swollen left eye and peered closely at the cabalistic bruise. The markings were letters. The word they formed was N–E–O–L–I–T–E.

Well, that figured. The original blunt instrument was undoubtedly a hillbilly sheriff.

166

After I'd rinsed off most of the blood and the boot prints, and dried myself on my shirt, I began to feel a bit more in touch with my surroundings. These, I noticed, seemed unusually quiet. No toilets flushing, no coughing and wheezing, no doors clanging, no idle chit-chat.

"Hey," I yelled through the bars, "anybody else in here?"

That drew no response, and neither did a ten-minute session of dragging a tin cup back and forth across the bars. I felt kind of silly, going through that tired old jail-house routine, but it usually guarantees you a little attention, even if it's nothing more than a bucketful of cold water tossed through the bars by an irritated guard. This time all I got out of it was a ringing in my ears. I seemed to be thoroughly alone.

There was no way of telling how long I'd been unconscious. Not only were my shoe laces, belt, and necktie missing, but I had also been relieved of my watch, presumably on the theory that I might somehow commit suicide with an Audemars-Piguet.

Along toward evening, the jail began showing signs of life. First, a turnkey wandered past my cell and informed me, with a snaggle-toothed grin, that I was a cinch to be sent to a work camp for passing forged checks. As evidence, they had the check I'd passed at the country store just before the lights went out, and they had the check protector and other things that I'd abandoned in Atlanta. That was nice.

A little later, an iron door opened some place and a line of prisoners marched past the front of my cell. They had been out working all day. Now they were back for the night, laughing, yelling, disrupting the peaceful quiet of the place, and showing little respect for the sorrows of a chap who had just been assured that he was on his way to a work camp.

167

There was nothing for it — I settled back into the old jail routine, making the best of it, and waiting to see what the future would bring.

I was stretched out on my bunk trying to see how large a slab of paint I could peel from the wall all in a single piece, when the native in the next compartment called over to me.

"Hey theah, Yankee boy, yew got yoh light on?"

"Yeah," I said, "Ah got mah light on."

"Good thing. Leave 'er on an' don' go to swattin' up on ol' Henry when he come by."

I rolled over and peered out into the corridor to see what old Henry looked like. My ribs still hurt like hell, and I was just about in the right mood to go to swattin' up on somebody if he turned out to be small enough. The corridor was empty. Presently, however, I detected movement at the lower edge of my vision and turned my gaze to the floor. A huge Cuban roach — Henry, presumably — was scurrying busily past my cell. He was manfully towing a great, long white thread, one end knotted about his midsection and the other trailing out of sight down the corridor behind him.

"Henry git by yew yit, Yankee boy?"

"Yeah," I said, pressing my cheek to the bars for a better angle. "He's almost past the cell beyond mine."

"Yew heah that, John Dee? Yankee boy says he almost theah."

"Ah see him, Billy Joe. Turn youah light out an' I'll send 'im back soon's I fetch up the thraid."

And that was the drill for the rest of my stay. Sometimes Billy Joe and John Dee would send cigarettes back and forth on the end of the thread that was costing ol' Henry so much labor, but most of the time they only made dry runs. It was all the same to Henry, though, because he always turned in at the first dark cell whether the string was loaded or not.

In all the jail house stories I'd heard of these nicotinic evangels, there was always an element of necessity; a pressing need for tobacco, and no possible way of transporting it. Then some wise old jail crow remembers the cockroach trick and solves the problem neatly. That makes for a nice, colorful bit of lore, but I've never seen the inside of a jail where it wouldn't have been far easier just to slide a butt along the floor, or even to ricochet it off the opposite wall. There was no question of necessity here. As a matter of fact, Henry was continually zigzagging in and out between my bars, in spite of the light I kept burning to warn him off the shoals, and I spent considerable time untangling the thread and setting the poor creature back on the proper course. An entirely useless endeavor, but it did kill a lot of time for John Dee and Billy Joe. And for me. I had to kill nearly two months before I was finally taken to court on the forgery charge.

Courtrooms — and I have been in a few of them — have a certain uniformity about them all across the country. I mean it's just like Perry Mason. There are always the benches for the spectators, the wooden railing that sets off the arena proper, with its tables for defense and prosecution, and the jury box is usually on the right as you face the raised bench of justice. Justice, herself, poor blind whore, is often depicted above that bench, with her balance scales all out of kilter from the endless tamperings of shyster defense counsels and conviction-hungry prosecutors. There is always the American flag to one side of the bench and the state flag to the other. And even with the musty smells, and the full knowledge of miscarriages for and against the com-

169

munity, and graft, and human failure, there is always a feeling of majesty about a courtroom; something that no superficial shabbiness can dispel.

But something was missing here. The courtroom looked like a Tennessee Williams stage setting, and somewhere between the folding chairs for the spectators and the bust of Jeff Davis that filled in for Justice, there was a distinctly unmajestic air to the place. This lack of grandeur and dignity was not helped by the presence, in one dim corner, of a popcorn machine. It was rather like being tried in the lobby of an all-night movie.

The solemnity of the proceedings was in keeping with the decor. I was escorted to the bench by the sheriff, who identified me to the judge as "the Yankee what swindled ol' Sy Oliver." All I could see of His Honor was a thatch of gray hair and two gray eyes that peered down at me without much interest from the rim of the seven-foot bench. It was the tallest judge's bench I'd ever seen in my life.

"Haow you pleadin', boy," the judge asked.

"Not guilty, your Honor."

"You tryin' to weasel out o' this heah charge, boy?"

"No, sir, your Honor," I said. "I just feel there are extenuating circumstances that should be brought to the Court's attention."

Actually, the circumstances I had in mind were no more than what any right-thinking thief would call upon in a court of law. The idea at a preliminary hearing of this sort is to deny your guilt and have yourself remanded back to the county jail. That gives you time to think of additional angles; and it gives the authorities time to weigh the expense of a trial against the wisdom of letting you cop a plea for a reduced sentence. I've known men who were so adept at gumming up the wheels of Justice that they succeeded in getting such charges as Murder and Criminal Assault broken down to Second Degree Mopery. Of course, there is risk in these tactics. If you are tried and found guilty, you can always count on receiving a far longer prison sentence than you would have gotten for pleading guilty in the first place. There are probably some soreheads who will contend that this basic American practice is nothing but a shady means of coercing the accused into an admission of guilt. But there *are* traditions of jurisprudence to be upheld, and it's unseemly for the layman to question them.

"You mean, boy, that y'all gonna stand there an' tell this Court that you want the State of Georgia to go to the expense o' givin' you a trial for somethin' you shore nuff did?"

Hah, thought I, it's going to work. The old boy is thinking about the taxpayers.

"I'm sorry about the expense, your Honor," I said, "and I regret the delay in these proceedings, but . . ."

"Don't fret none over that, boy. Ain't gonna be no delay." The judge's head disappeared momentarily from the ramparts, and he called out to someone in the back room. "Bailiff! Court's in session. Check over them jury rolls."

I could hear someone grumbling in reply and the unmistakable sound of a cork being slapped into a jug. A moment later, a gaunt and seedy individual in a shoelace necktie came around from behind the bench, gave me a bleary glare, and reeled on out of the courtroom.

He was back in less than two minutes with the jury. Obviously, he had impaneled them from the citizens who took their leisure — 24 hours a day, apparently — on the benches in the square.

There is much that can be said for the jury system in this country — and there is much that can be said against it. Certainly it's better to be judged by an average group of

171

citizens than to place your liberty in the arbitrary hands of a single individual; especially if that individual is a professional dispenser of justice, grown callous — and possibly corrupt — from too many years and too much power. With a jury, at least, there is always the hope that the prejudices and human weaknesses of one individual will counterbalance those of another, and that the less tarnished ideals of citizenship will contribute to a conscientious effort toward honest judgement.

But, contrary to the simple-minded idiocies taught in our high schools, no jury in the world arrives at its verdict through a cold and impartial assessment of the facts. The findings are based on emotional responses to everything from the number of warts on the nose of the accused, to the dramatic quality of the prosecutor's performance. Consequently, the selection of a jury is critically important in any criminal case. If the accused is an attractive young woman, counsel for the defense makes a determined effort to seed the jury box with men who will be sympathetically inclined toward helpless beauty, while the prosecutor will do his damnedest to cinch a conviction by running in a jury of bitterly jealous old women. The right and the wrong of the thing, the guilty or not guilty, has little to do with the outcome of a jury trial.

And when I saw my jury in that Georgia courtroom, I had no doubt what the final verdict would be.

Ask any man in prison to describe his jury for you and he will draw a vivid picture of 12 sodden hicks with bib overalls, red-wool long-johns showing at their collars, dung-spattered boots (if he credits them with being shod), and tobacco juice dribbling down their unshaven chins. Honesty compels me to admit that my jury wasn't like that at all. No, indeed. There were only *six* of them on my jury.

172

The trial itself was not one of those frivolous northern affairs, with reams of testimony from prosecution and defense witnesses, with charges and rebuttals, examinations and cross-examinations, exhibits of evidence, recesses, objections, and all the many fripperies of Blackstone. There was not even a prosecutor. And, since Gideon had not yet blown his trumpet in Florida, forcing the Supreme Court ruling that all accused persons must be furnished with counsel, no one seemed to think it necessary that I should have a lawyer. Not that Clarence Darrow, himself, could have done me any good in *that* courtroom. The only laws I heard quoted seemed to have derived from the code duello.

In keeping with the general informality of the hearing, the judge addressed each juror by name — "Ha theah, Harry. Haow's the waife an' kids? Haow you, Clem? Crops doin' awright, John D?" — and patiently explained to them how I had come all the way from up north just to spread financial ruin among the local citizens.

With the details of my crime certified as gospel, I was allowed to take the stand and claim my innocence. This I did most vehemently, tossing in such mitigating tidbits as my rural upbringing, my fear of God, and a dearly beloved grandmother who hailed from the great State of Georgia. But the jury sat walleyed through my performance, and it was easy to see they were not impressed.

I stepped down from the stand, and ol' Sy Oliver got up and told his story of the infamous robbery. He was magnificent. With tears running down his cheeks, he explained to his neighbors how that check would have driven his store into bankruptcy, how his wife would have had to go back to pulling a plow, and how his orphaned children would have wandered the streets homeless until starvation overtook them. By the time he was through, I had a lump in my

173

throat the size of a honeydew melon — at the thought of my own prospects, you understand.

Finally the judge charged the jury. He explained that they could find me either innocent or guilty, but that any-one who voted for acquittal would sure roast in hell — not to mention having his crops fail and his daughter marry a nigger — for betraying his neighbors and the sovereign State of Georgia. They found me guilty without even leav-ing the courtroom.

And, just like that, I had myself one to two years at hard labor.

CHAPTER FOURTEEN

A little old man in the Scranton County lockup once told me, "Son, don't ever get your Yankee ass in a hillbilly jail." I finally learned the wisdom of this fatherly advice when they packed me up for delivery to the road camp. The place where they were sending me wasn't exactly a modern facility. It was an old turpentine ranch that has been in constant use for the past 60 years.

Back in the early 1900's, turpentine stills were spotted all over south Georgia and Alabama in the pine forests and swamps that cover that country. Private companies used to lease a few thousand acres and bleed the trees dry with convict labor, which was also leased from the state. When the trees and the convicts were all depleted, the turpentine people would move on, and the lumber people would move in.

Today, there is nothing much left in those parts to attract private industry — just a profitless expanse of mangrove, knotted-pine stumps, and mud — but there is still plenty of work there for Georgia's convicts. The only difference is that there are no more two-dollar-a-day jobs as leased labor under adequately paid and trained civilians. Now the work consists of half-hearted, state-organized, land-reclamation projects, road maintenance, and an ineffectual reforestation program.

The chain gangs of those early years are also largely a thing of the past. Someone finally realized that men can't work efficiently when they're wearing leg irons. But nothing else has changed much in those work camps.

When the sheriff delivered me and two Negro marijuana farmers to that old turpentine camp, he might have been driving us straight into the 1920's — and his creaking old Model A panel truck with the bird-cage doors and the floppy fenders would have been right at home in that period. The camp was a compound, 50 yards square, enclosed by a single strand of barbed wire like you might find around a pasture. Its only real purpose was to mark off the camp boundaries and to separate it from the drab expanse of swamp that stretched for ten or 15 miles on all sides.

The compound contained a haphazard assortment of wooden buildings. The largest was the "cage," a heavily-barred barracks for the convicts. Right beside it was the mess shack, and beside that was the cook shack. At one end of the compound there was a fenced enclosure and a row of kennels for the camp dogs. At the far end was the head-quarters shack, a few storage sheds and the blacksmith shop — which was really no more than a tool shed.

Looking at that unpainted clapboard dungeon, I didn't feel much of anything except curiosity. I had been hearing about chain gangs all my life, about the colorful striped clothes, the man-eating cockroaches, and how they locked you up in chains and threw away the warden. They had me scheduled for a year's vacation in this place, so now, at least,

176

I would be able to fill out a gap in my education that hadn't been covered by run-of-the-mill prisons and jails.

My education began in earnest when the sheriff turned me over to the Captain in charge of the camp. This man was known to guards and convicts alike as Old Jay Dee. He was a large man in his late 50's, with an exceptionally long, red face, almost chinless, and with immense protruding eyes. If you had looped chains from his ears he would have passed for a fire hydrant.

"Waal, Sam," he asked the sheriff, "what we got hyah?"

"Two niggahs and one Yankee. Mr. Hot-Stuff, here, cashed a rubber check on ol' Sy Oliver owns the mercantile 'stablishment over at Claymore Corners."

"Sure 'nuff? What the niggahs do?"

"They just growed themselves a little hemp. Jedge figured they oughta have about six months on the road to teach 'em the value of real tobacco," said the sheriff.

The Captain wasn't listening. He was walking a small circle around me, like I was General Sherman and he was looking for my matches.

"Doggone," he said, "a real Yankee. Been seven, eight year since we had one o' them down hyah."

He smiled at me then, a fire hydrant with teeth. "Lemme tell you, boy, this hyah is a road camp, and y'all wanna keep yoah nose clean if you wanna get back up Nawth. We don't think much of no smartass Yankees come down hyah and deprivin' folk of their livelihood. No. Don't say nothin', boy. I know your wuthless, carpetbaggin' type, and we know how to deal with you down hyah."

He continued in this vein for a good five minutes. He had a double-barrelled shotgun in his hands and when he wanted to emphasize a point he thumped the butt of it against the ground. By the time he had flailed up a good cloud of dust,

he was well on the way to making a believer of me. I didn't
out and out apologize for being born in Michigan, but I sure
went along meekly when he sent me off with a guard to be
fitted with prison dungarees and assigned to a bunk in the
cage.

I found a friend in the camp almost immediately, a huge
Negro the color of raw umber. His name was Clyde, and he
had one of those fey senses of humor so often attributed to,
but so rarely encountered in, people who have been getting
stepped on most of their lives. It was hard to imagine anyone willfully stepping on Clyde's six foot four inches of bull
strength, but that's just what those hillbillys did. He caught
all of the heavy work and much of the abuse. Clyde didn't
like the treatment any more than anyone else would. He
simply had an abundance of good-natured patience, and up
to the last I heard of him, he still hadn't killed anybody.

When they first threw me in the cage and assigned me the
bunk next to Clyde, we found we had too much in common
not to hit it off. The guards had him pegged as a "rogue
niggah." And I was the camp Yankee — which put me just
one notch below Clyde. So we pulled all our details together, and worked together on the road gang, which was a
break for me. I had a lot to learn about jailing it on the
road.

The first thing I learned was that the term road gang is
very loosely applied. The one I was on was yanking stumps
out of the swamp to make room for a dredger. The idea was
to hammer the stumps out with a short, blunt instrument,
known locally as a stump axe. This was done in water that
might be up to your ankles or up to your chin, with the
depth changing at every floundering step. There was also
considerable mud. Whenever you set foot in this slop, you
liberated about a cubic yard of sulfur dioxide. And when

178

you were working in deep water, it came belching up to the surface in great flatulent bubbles that usually burst right under your nose.

I worked on that road gang for two months before I ever saw a road. It passed through the middle of the swamp we were clearing, and it was the most beautiful stretch of solid ground I'd ever seen. Before long I was bashing away at stumps with great enthusiasm, anxious to work my way to that road bank. Through the intervening mangroves, I could catch glimpses of bright cars speeding past, coming from faraway places and heading, perhaps, for places still further away. It had occurred to me that I might find an opportunity to do the same thing.

Clyde must have seen the faraway look in my eyes, or guessed the reason for my unlikely energy. He buried the head of his axe in a rotting log and sat down beside it to wipe the sweat from his face.

"It ain't no use, man," he said. "By the time we gets to that road, the old Captain he got maybe two, three shotguns on the bank. You just behave and you won't no more'n get your picture took."

"My picture?"

"Yeah, man, them tourists digs us a whole lot."

We spent two weeks working alongside that road bank, and I found out that Clyde was dead right — both about the Captain's foresight and about the tourists. Georgia convicts are regarded as a natural resource, almost as much a part of the scenery as a natural rock bridge, or a waterfall, or similar attractions that might come hemstitched onto a pillow. We had our pictures taken by every other carload of tourists that came by. Most of them only slowed down enough to snap away at us through their windows, but many stopped and asked the guards to move closer to where we were working and to hold their shotguns in a more alert attitude. Then they would stand around and talk about us in the third person, asking the guards how much work we did, what sort of sanitary facilities we had, and how we got along without women. One old fat doll, with an expensive Hasselblad, even managed to lower herself to the bottom of the embankment near where I was working and asked the guard to have me turn my back to her. She seemed convinced that I'd have a lot of picturesque whip marks across my shoulders.

Nearly all of these leeches, as I was continually reminded by the other men, were northerners; fellow Yankees who thought a chain gang was the most colorful thing this side of an Indian reservation. But while I was trying to figure out why anyone would want to take a picture of a lot of raggedy-assed convicts up to their ears in a swamp, most of the other cons were amusing themselves at the tourists' expense. We weren't allowed to say a word to them, but when the guards were busy shilling a new bunch, it was easy enough to aim a few pointed vulgarities at the female tourists. These crude remarks served both to give the men an outlet of sorts and to send the tourists scurrying, with their hair on end.

Clyde was more subtle. He thoroughly enjoyed having his picture taken, and he absolutely reveled in the attention he received. He was a genius at Uncle Tomming; playing the part of a foot-shuffling, forelock-tugging, old family retainer type, plantation darky. Out in the swamp or back in the cage, Clyde sang gutty old prison ballads and some of the most profane blues I've ever heard. For the tourists, he sang spirituals, crossing-over-Jordan, and lawd-but-ain't-this-cotton-heavy, and all that kind of rot. When he ran out of legitimate spirituals, he would use the melodies of the

180

dirty songs he sang in the cage and just mumble the lyrics.

One afternoon, Clyde caught a tourist who claimed to be a professor from Columbia University. He had a tape recorder, and he paid the gun guard five dollars to let him put Clyde on tape. Clyde obliged him by mumbling all the dirty songs he had ever heard, and for good measure he threw in a few variations on "Roll Me Over in the Clover." The professor was practically delirious at having discovered such a rare example of authentic folk art.

At the end of our two weeks by the embankment, however, I was happy to get back into the swamps and away from the tourists. The only thing I really missed was the food that Clyde had been getting from them.

There are many things about a prison, and especially about a road camp, that a man finds hard to take. But the worst, I'm sure, is the pure, unadulterated horror of grits and molasses for breakfast. Also for lunch and supper every day. For the last two meals, at least, we could usually count on black-eyed peas, as well. This diet was saved from monotony only through the addition of an occasional slab of sowbelly, which was really more of a challenge than a treat.

We were, however, allowed to supplement our fare with a little foraging. When we broke off for noon meal, the guards let us cook any wildlife we had managed to catch while working. All we had to do was find enough dry wood and enough dry ground to build a fire. This wildlife was available in appalling quantities and a wide selection of species. Every noon, you could just about take your pick from rabbits, opossums, muskrats, frogs, turtles, water moccasins, and a whole flock of things too far gone to identify. They had usually been killed with stump axes.

Clyde was a frog fancier. He used to spear them with a

181

sharpened stick, then hold them against the bole of a tree with his left hand while he severed the legs with a deft blow of his axe. He skinned them and ate them on the spot, raw and kicking. Clyde had wonderful manners and he always offered one of the legs to me, with repeated assurances that down in his bayou country everyone ate them that way. I declined.

To Clyde, a frog was a "swamp dog," while anything not normally accepted as table fare was a "critter." Every other day he would come sloshing up to announce, "The boys has got theirselves a critter. C'mon, man, we is eatin'." I'd tag along, more out of curiosity than hunger, just to see what new marvel they had pulled squirming from the muck. I figured if it ever turned out to be too extreme for consumption someone should be there to report it to the Museum of Natural History.

The only time I took part in these Paleozoic picnics was when the food was recognizably mammalian. I made an eager exception for terrapin. Clyde and a couple of other Negroes had a knack for gutting these and roasting them in their own shells. I've never since tasted anything quite so delicious.

One time we had a deer. A guard we called Snake Eyes saw it moving in the bushes and mistook it for a convict. He let us carry it back to camp, and everyone from the Captain on down to Clyde and me had a fine meal. Everyone except Snake Eyes; he was so disappointed to find he'd only shot a deer that he couldn't touch a mouthful.

Snake Eyes was as mean a cuss as ever sought employment as a prison guard, but when he wasn't right on your back it was hard to take him seriously. He was a gangly man with jug-handle ears, and knotty muscles on his jaws that made him look like he was always gritting his teeth on a mouthful of hickory nuts. His eyes all but overlapped, and he walked with a heavy limp — according to camp rumor he had badly gashed his foot when one of his socks broke.

If there was one redeeming quality about Snake Eyes, it was probably his sincere appreciation of good liquor. Anyone who cultivates the finer things in life can't be completely bad. Of course, he couldn't really afford *good* liquor, so he settled for white lightning, real honest-to-god squeezings that one of his cousins drizzled out of a still back in the swamps. He used to bring this stuff to work in a Mason jar. If there is any such thing as a true and enduring tradition of the South, that's it — a Mason jar full of mule. The extraordinary thing, though, was his insistence that the jar never contained anything but turpentine.

Snake Eyes claimed that he had to drink turpentine as a physic. He nipped on this stuff all day long and at noon, when the rest of us sat down to our grits and critters, he would pull a fatback sandwich and that Mason jar out of his overalls jacket and really get to work. He used to toast us with that jar before he started. "Turpentine," he'd say, "the best thing in the world for what ails you, boys."

One day when we were out in the swamp, Snake Eyes was given an opportunity to test that theory quite literally. While he was taking his hourly inventory of inmates, a couple of guards from another work detail slipped over and tapped his Mason jar. After they had consumed all of the mule, they replaced it with a full measure of genuine turpentine. When Snake Eyes returned later — with a massive thirst — he swallowed half the jar before he loosed a strangled shriek: "Some bastard's put turpentine in my turpentine!"

The Captain was another man who didn't mind an occasional snort, but he suffered from an ulcer that would just

183

barely tolerate alcohol — one good jolt of pure swamp mule probably would have perforated his stomach canker and spared everyone a lot of trouble. The Captain, however, was a man of infinite resource and cunning. He had discovered a formula that allowed him to smuggle alcohol past his ulcer in sufficient quantities to achieve a continual glow. His secret was a 50-50 mixture of milk and Hadacol, a popular snake liniment that assayed out at 32 proof. It was this stuff that brought me as close as I ever came to a real old-time chain gang.

Clyde and I were standing outside the headquarters shack one evening during our one-hour exercise period. We were out of bounds, because we weren't supposed to go more than 50 feet from the cage, but no one ever said anything if you drifted over toward headquarters. Men were always going back and forth between there and the cage, either called over for a chewing out or going on their own to ask a favor or to deliver a tip.

We were just enjoying the last few minutes of evening coolness before the mosquitoes began boiling up out of the swamp, when Clyde called my attention to the Captain's window. Through the unscreened opening I could see Old Jay Dee tilted back in his chair with his feet on the desk. He was dead asleep. And on a small table just inside the window I could see two bottles of 32-proof nectar. We didn't bother discussing the matter, and we didn't wait to plan the caper with the care it deserved. Clyde just stretched one of his long arms through the window and quietly gathered up both bottles. He tossed one to me, and we headed back to the cage with the loot under our shirts.

When the Captain found his Hadacol missing, he screamed like a cow moose brought to childbed. This was one hour after we clipped him, and we hadn't figured on the loss being noticed until he came back to work the next day. By then it would have been too late to do anything about it. As it was, the bulls rousted everyone out of the cage and began checking breaths about five minutes after Clyde and I had finished off the goodies. It didn't take much of an investigation to pick us out of that line-up.

The Captain didn't say anything until he got us into his shack, then he cut loose on us with some of the finest invective I've ever heard. He traced Clyde's haphazardly improbable ancestry all the way back to the Congo, and he called me everything but white. You'd have thought we'd challenged the power of prayer.

Finally he said, in a very reasonable tone of voice, "I s'pose you craven sons-of-bitches think I'm going to give you a couple months or so in the mother-rotten sweatbox for that stunt?"

I tried to look meek, and Clyde allowed as to how we most surely deserved that much. He was going into his foot-shuffling bit, and I figured he might at least Uncle Tom us down to two weeks.

"Well, you bastards are wrong as hell," the Captain continued. "You're going to keep right on choppin' stumps; 'ceptin' for the next three month you'll damn well do it in chains." He looked directly at me and I guess I wasn't looking convinced, what with it actually against the law and all, which caused him to add, "An' you damn well bet I'm serious, boy. If I tell y'all a chicken dips snuff, you look under his wing and that's where the can'll be!"

And that's where the can was. The law be damned. Four guards escorted us to the tool shed where a trusty rummaged around in a clutter of old shovels and picks, broken halters, saws, files, and rusted pieces of farm machinery, and produced a five-foot length of log chain with a leg

185

shackle on each end. These things didn't snap on or lock like handcuffs. They put me on a stool and hauled my left foot up on an anvil. The shackle was sprung enough to slide over my foot. Once it was in place, they forced it shut with a C-clamp and fixed it that way with a red-hot, half-inch rivet. The riveting only took a few seconds and, before the shackle really had a chance to burn its way down to bone, they dumped a bucket of water over the whole operation. Then they gave Clyde the same routine on the right ankle.

This turned out to be very inconvenient. Just dragging a log chain around is awkward enough, but when you have someone on the other end, who outweighs you by 70 pounds, it gets to be a real burden. Clyde used to thresh about in his sleep, and he was continually yanking me out of bed. For awhile after they first put the chains on us, he sometimes forgot all about me even when he was awake. We would be standing around scraping muck off our shoes, or just admiring the swamp, and Clyde would blithely start off for someplace else.

After a while, though, we achieved a certain skill at maneuvering our iron umbilicus around stumps and snags and other convicts. We were like a precision drill team. When we were moving, one of us automatically hooked up the chain on his stump axe, and Clyde learned to chop left-handed so that we could work on the same stump without taking my head off.

There were still the inconveniences, of course — like getting a leg pulled out of joint in the middle of the night, and accompanying one another to the john, and having to wash our trousers in the swamp without being able to re-move them — but it wasn't half the punishment the Cap-tain thought it was. For one thing, being in chains already, nobody worried too much about what we were doing. And the guards didn't expect us to get too many stumps. There was also one very tangible benefit; Maudie-Mae.

Maudie-Mae was Clyde's wife, and she came to see him faithfully every Sunday afternoon, the only time visitors were allowed at the camp. Since I was so firmly attached to Clyde, this meant that I would necessarily have to accompany him on his visits and share the lunch basket that Maudie always brought him.

All visits at the camp were held through a screen, with the convicts seated in the mess hall and the visitors on the other side of a barrier that ran the length of the room and about five feet from one wall. When a visitor was escorted into this corridor, any lunch baskets intended for convicts were appropriated, carefully checked for contraband, and then delivered on the other side of the screen by one of the guards or a trusty. Clyde had mentioned a couple of times that Maudie was one heck of a cook, but since he wasn't allowed to carry any of the food away from a visit to share with me, he very thoughtfully had avoided going into detail. Now that the administration had so kindly cut me in on the action, it was all I could do to muster enough tact not to hound him on the subject.

When Maudie showed up for that first joint visit, I felt like nothing less than one long gut. All that week, I had been conjuring up visions of crackling fried chicken, homemade bread, buttered turnip greens, and candied yams. I had almost worked up a strong affection for the South and its culinary traditions. I mean, just because they had spawned sowbelly and grits, that didn't mean they were *all* a bunch of slobs.

Clyde introduced me to Maudie, an exceedingly buxom and handsome woman who was two or three shades blacker than he was. She was warm and friendly and completely at

187

ease, as though her husband always walked around with a strange white man chained to him. I'm afraid, though, I wasn't giving this unusual woman the full attention she deserved. I had my eye on the trusty who was bringing the basket of food, and all I could see for Maudie-Mae was a huge piece of fried chicken.

Dear old understanding Clyde didn't keep me waiting. As soon as the basket arrived, he removed the cover and began spreading that southern cooking out in front of us.

There was no fried chicken. To my unutterable stupefaction, our meal was Sauerbraten and Kartoffelkloessen.

Maudie-Mae was, indeed, a very unusual woman. Until 1938, Maudie had worked for ten years at a luxury hotel in Hamburg. She had originally gone there in 1928, with her father, who was employed as a butler by Graf von Tromanhauser. When her father died, and Maudie began to notice that even white Jews were leaving for more congenial surroundings, she surmised it was certainly time for a Negress to pull out.

So there I sat in a Georgia prison camp, eating Sauerbraten and listening to a Negro woman recite Heine in beautifully accented German. And I suppose what made it even more unlikely was the gin.

Having been locked up for some time, I noticed right away that Maudie had enormous breasts. These seemed even more prominent after she sat down. On the visitors' side of the screen, a narrow shelf ran the length of the barrier at tabletop height. When Clyde and I had finished the food, Maudie placed her purse on the shelf on one side of her and her coat on the other. Then she spread her bosom out in the middle and canted herself forward. The effect was startling.

It was even more startling when she drew an ordinary soda

straw from her purse and thrust one end into her imposing cleavage. The other end fit neatly through the quarter-inch mesh of the screen that separated us.

Clyde nudged me and looked around for the guard. "Go ahead, man. You first," he said.

Maudie-Mae was smiling encouragingly, and I didn't want to offend anyone on top of that Sauerbraten, so what the hell. I sucked gently at the straw and was rewarded with a good slug of gin. My respect for Maudie-Mae went up another couple of notches.

For the rest of the afternoon, Clyde and I took turns on the gin straw, getting mellower and mellower. Where we had been pals before, now we were practically litter mates.

"Man, old buddy-boy," Clyde said, "this is really jailin' it, huh?" Then he grinned at me, "But you just pull on that there gin and don't be eye-ballin' my woman."

The more gin I got into me, the harder it was to follow this admonition. My eyes had a tendency to cross down the length of that straw, down into the dark, gin-giving depths of Maudie's bosom. She had quite the largest breasts I had ever seen on a woman, and they kept getting bigger all the time.

And this was the weirdest part of all. Over the next couple of months — and quite in spite of myself — I seemed to have developed a strange sort of mother fixation on Maudie-Mae. It got to the point where every time I thought of liquor, I thought of Maudie's mammaries. And every time I thought of Maudie, I wanted a drink.

At length, I hesitantly mentioned this Freudian tidbit to Clyde. "That's alright, brother John," he said pleasantly. "Just as long as you don't get no more'n that straw in your teeth."

189

CHAPTER FIFTEEN

One thing all the road camps had in common was dogs. They were used both for intimidation and for tracking down runaways; they performed the first function with occasional success and the second with absolute brilliance. I've known men who used every devious trick imaginable to lose those camp dogs in a swamp; from swimming underwater to sprinkling pepper on their back trail. Nothing seemed to fool those animals, though there was never any shortage of convicts with revolutionary and infallible techniques for giving them the slip. It was while I was in the old turpentine camp, for instance, that the TV hucksters first came up with their ballyhoo for chlorophyll as a deodorizing agent. According to the claims, even if your breath was enough to gag a maggot, this stuff would make you the kissable queen of the J-Hop, and the funkiest case of lumberjack's armpit would turn to violets. Chlorophyll was the magic ingredient — one dose and the most sensitive nose couldn't recognize you as human. Almost overnight, it be-

came known to almost every convict in the southern states
that this was a sure ticket past the dogs.

So far as I know, the first man with enough empiricism
in his soul to offer himself up for the cause of freedom was
a skinny ridgerunner they called Rabbitfoot. He had spent
a total of 12 years in the camps and had 19 escape attempts
against him. He had made it twice, though never for long,
because it was easier for the law to catch him out of the
swamp than in it. Aside from being the skinniest man in the
State of Georgia, he had the reddest hair and the spottiest
freckles I'd ever seen. Rabbitfoot had the right idea —
there just wasn't any place he could go looking like an
extraterrestrial.

None of the commercially available preparations of
chlorophyll had yet penetrated to our swampy fastness, so
Rabbitfoot had to improvise. He used grass. And for anyone who might be tempted to duplicate the experiment, I
will point out that there are probably better ways to obtain
chlorophyll. Rabbitfoot was assigned to a perpetual dish-
washing detail in the mess shack, because the Captain had
it figured that no one that skinny could steal much food.
This gave him access to the meat grinder that was used for
pre-masticating our boarhide and sowbelly.

For two weeks, Rabbitfoot smuggled huge quantities of
grass into the mess shack, where he pulped it in the meat
grinder and squeezed the juice off into one of the Captain's
old Hadacol bottles. Everybody knew when he had the bottle full, because our sowbelly reverted to its usual lighter
shade of green. I noticed, too, that all through the experiment our sowbelly had exuded the same rancid odor as
always, notwithstanding the generous addition of pure
chlorophyll. This plainly boded ill for Rabbitfoot's chances
of success.

191

Rabbitfoot made his break on a Friday evening when most of the guards were off duty, ministering to their thirsts. He slipped out of the cook shack just after seven o'clock count and waded off into the swamp, manfully chewing a mouthful of grass and washing it down with the greenish crap in the Hadacol bottle. He had also sprinkled the stuff on his clothing and rubbed it into his skin. He was a blotchy, red-and-green swamp specter, a nameless something belched up out of the mud. Some of the guys were making book that if he didn't shake off the dogs, he would at least be able to scare them back to the camp.

The guards were after Rabbitfoot within the hour. And it didn't take the dogs more than five minutes to find the trail. The entire pack caught up with Rabbitfoot two miles from camp. He was sitting on a stump, being very sick, and for two months afterward he was subject to fits of nausea at the mere mention of grass.

As keen-scented as they were, the Georgia camp dogs were a great disappointment to me. I had been a life-long adherent of the bloodhound myth, and when I thought of prison dogs — which I am the first to admit wasn't very often — I thought of noble purebreds, with ears down to their hind quarters and practically tripping over their own dewlaps as they belled the trail of some fugitive. This is not an uncommon misconception, since the word "bloodhound" has fallen upon rather careless usage.

Actually, blooded hounds are as rarely encountered around prison camps as the giant squid. All the dogs I saw were of the most wildly bastardized and bitched-up breeds ever to raid a garbage can. There were great hulking brutes clearly descended from Irish wolfhounds, slatternly assortments of ribs escaped from some sharecropper's chicken yard, and a few that were actually indistinguishable from cats. While I was there, the dominant strain was coon dog, but even that time-honored term had come into somewhat cavalier usage. There was one guard at the camp who used to hunt coon with a dog that was 90 percent Boston bull.

This herd of dissipated dogflesh was more or less self-perpetuating, though it was bolstered up from time to time with reserves scraped from various pounds, and by donations that resulted when some horny mongrel got into a farmer's blooded bitch. Most of this misbegotten pack was kept in a pen at the far end of the camp. When there was an escape, the lot of them would be released. Any dog too stupid or citified to follow a convict could at least follow the other dogs and contribute to the yapping.

One dog out of this pack was allowed the freedom of the camp. He was a huge yellow mongrel, something between a redbone, a Dobermann and a police dog — and I think it was the police dog in him that appealed to the Captain.

"That there animal is nigh pure German shepherd," he used to boast. "And trained — boy, they don't come no bettern. Here, you old son-of-a-bitch, come to heel!" And the brute would bare his fangs and look around for a convict to bite.

Aside from enjoying the Captain's confidence, this beast had another singular distinction. His name was God. Obviously this is just plain *dog* spelled backwards, but the effect was startling. For some of the colored men in camp who had been raised on the Old Testament, it was downright terrifying. It was also considerably ironic when Old Jay Dee would stand out behind our barracks and bellow:

"God! Come to me, God! *GOD,* you mangy son of a bitch, where the hell are you?"

There were a lot of us chained in that rotten cage who used to wonder exactly the same thing.

Perhaps it was God's continual association with the Captain, or maybe it was just because he enjoyed so much freedom, but whatever it was, he was devoutly hated by every man in the camp. His general viciousness, of course, did nothing to improve his standing. God wasn't mean in the savage sense that is associated with a wild beast. There is a certain nobility about that. No, God's was a stupid, glowering, skulking meanness that would have been called sadism in a man.

God couldn't bother most of us, because we divided all our time between the swamp and the cage. But he struck cold fear into the heart of the camp workers. God was the scourge of the trusty inmates, and the most sorely put upon of these was Homer.

Homer was an Atlanta burglar still in his early 20's, a decent lad, with an engaging smile and the look of a college boy, who was pulling his first prison time. He was the slop man, the one who brought the buckets of grits and peas from the mess shack to the cage. This earned him a good deal of abuse from the riffraff who held him personally responsible for all the wrongs done to that sowbelly by everyone from the administration on down to a one-eyed cook who couldn't tell a chitlin from a goober pea. Homer took all this with an easy grace, realizing that the men were just letting off pressure. But he didn't take to God with any semblance of grace.

God used to lay for Homer just outside the cage, and when Homer came trundling along, his cart full of atrocities, God would show his awful fangs and snarl until Homer set him down a bowl of beans and fatback. The stupid brute never felt a bit of gratitude. He accepted the offering as his due and looked at Homer like he was a long-lost bone. Any normal animal would have learned to wag its

194

tail at the sight of its meal ticket. But not God. With him it was always a shakedown. "A tithing," Homer used to call it.

Eventually this shameless extortion came to be too much, even for the gentle Homer. He decided to poison God.

The most convenient and traditional poison at hand was glass. Homer gathered a few hot-sauce bottles, dumped them into an old sock, and mashed them up with a rock. The result was ground glass, and we all firmly believed it was the deadliest substance this side of Lucretia Borgia. Homer mixed nearly half a pound of this stuff with an equal amount of sowbelly — and when God next waylaid him, just before evening chow, Homer placed it gingerly in front of him.

Everyone in the cage knew what was happening and heartily endorsed the execution. We were all at the windows watching as God clomped over to the deadly mixture and sniffed it suspiciously. Anyway, everyone figured he was *supposed* to sniff it suspiciously. Actually, he bolted it down as swiftly as ever. From where I was sitting at one of the cage windows, it sounded as though the wretched beast were eating gravel. It was either a very inferior grade of hot-sauce bottle, or a pretty sloppy job of grinding.

We all spent a good deal of time, the next few days, watching God with a sharply clinical interest. Some of the fellows got up a pool to see who could come closest to the final hour. But nothing happened. God passed that glass like it was castor oil and came back for more sowbelly. Homer obliged him, but with diminishing enthusiasm. For all of a week, that animal walked around with enough silica in his alimentary canal to make a greenhouse.

Then Homer cut his hand on one of the hot-sauce bottles and got blood poisoning. He swore it was retribution, and

195

gave up. If he'd been free he probably would have turned himself in at the nearest monastery.

Even though God survived like a true immortal, I had been surprised to find that I could wish so sincerely for any dog's death, since I have always been ridiculously fond of animals. But I had seen some of the men brought back after God had tracked them down. I still think more of men than I do of dogs. And damn all that trash about it being a dog's instinct to hunt, even if the quarry is a man. I figured God was a bastard no matter how you cut it. Besides, the jerk got a can of Red Heart dog food every day and I had jolly little sympathy for anyone who was eating better than I was.

The Captain *had* lost one good lead dog a few years earlier though, when he forced the job of dog boy on an old-time thief named Jertha. Around southern prisons, dog boys are even more hated than screws or snitches because, in most cases, they combine all the more revolting qualities of both. They are usually chosen, in the first place, because of their willingness to cooperate with the administration. In any case, the nature of the job forces them into intimacy with the keepers, and it seldom takes long for the isolation of their position to divorce them from the other convicts. They spend a very lonely time with their precious trust; pampering and feeding and training the animals that will hunt down their fellow convicts.

Jertha was a good thief and a solid convict, and he didn't want any part of a deal like that. But the Captain had it in his head that Jertha would make a good screw — either that, or finish out his three-year sentence in the sweatbox, which would have been a whole lot more unpleasant than being thought a snitch. So, when tears and lamentations and threats of revenge had no effect, Jertha became the Captain's dog boy. For exactly one week.

196

Jertha stayed with the job just long enough to make friends with the dogs. When he figured he was buddy-buddy enough with the mutts that they wouldn't eat him, he turned the whole bunch loose one night and escaped into the swamp, taking the lead dog with him on a leash.

Old Cap really went to storming and fuming over that one. Even a dragooned dog boy is not supposed to violate his sacred trust, and he damn sure isn't supposed to run off with the Captain's prize dog. The double loss, and the twitting from the sheriff, was almost more than Cap could bear, and he was still cursing Jertha's eyes a month later, when the local freight agent called and told him for God's sake to come down and pick up a crate that was running everybody out of the depot. The thing smelled so bad it had taken three niggers and a bull whip to kick it out of the freight car onto the loading dock.

Cap picked a strong stomach from his personnel roster and sent it down to bury the box without even opening it. He knew without looking that Jertha had sent back his best lead dog. He was mad as hell, but not particularly surprised, because escapees and ex-cons were always mailing him little tokens of appreciation, such as rattlesnakes and armadillos and dead opossums.

I couldn't help thinking that it must be hell to be the sort of person who inspires people to send dead or poisonous gifts, and I could almost feel a little sorry for the Captain. But not much.

There was another dog in the camp that finally got me into a lot of trouble. He was a nondescript canine blob that went by the name of Bolsich. And this wasn't because he'd had a borzoi in his woodpile, either. Bolsich had earned his name because he devoted his few waking hours to biting and scratching at a chronic itch in a very sensitive location.

If you got up close enough to this animal, so that you could call him without attracting guffaws from all over the camp, it was possible to dissuade him momentarily from his psychosomatic flea. But neither sowbelly nor sweet talk would hold his attention. He just looked up sadly, with two of the most haunted and watery eyes in dogdom, then returned to his pursuit.

For reasons of his own, the Captain allowed Bolsich to live right in his office shack, and that's where I met him.

Our paths crossed six months after I came to the camp, when the Captain found out I knew how to type. He called me into his shack one morning and favored me with a long, fishy stare. Then he opened up that little hole in his long red face and said, "Boy, how'd you like to get off that there gang?"

"Yes, suh," I shot right back, being careful not to overdo the southern accent I'd been cultivating for the past few months. "I sure would like to get off that there gang, Captain."

"Well, boy, I understand y'all know how to work one of them things yonder." He pointed to the abandoned ruin of an old Oliver typewriter that was quietly falling apart in a dark corner. It obviously hadn't seen service for at least two decades, but it looked as though it might be coaxed into producing five or ten words a minute — if I could find any tools to repair it.

When I allowed as how I could work the machine over yonder, he actually got up and clapped me on the shoulder.

"Boy," he said, treating me to a breath full of Hadacol and warm milk, "I'm makin' you my secratree. You just clean out that there corner, and keep yo' nose clean, and I'll see y'all get took care of."

I didn't get took care of, exactly, but at least the guards

198

let up on me for being a Yankee, since I was so close to the throne. And there was nothing exciting about the work. On the order of three times a week, Old Jay Dee would think of a pretext for writing an official letter to someone. And twice a week he would issue a departmental memorandum to stick on the bulletin boards in the shack and in the barracks. No one ever answered the letters, and no one ever paid any attention to the memos, probably because they couldn't read them. There didn't seem to be many people around who could read even simple English, and the Captain had a passion for long words. He always insisted that I use the longest, most God-forsaken words in the language. Sometimes he would take a finished memo or letter and go over it putting in synonyms that he looked up in "Rawjets Theesarius," with the typical illiterate's disregard for connotation.

Aside from these infrequent diversions, I had a pretty dull time of it. The Captain didn't hold much for a lot of jawin', and there was never anything in the shack to read except an old copy of the *Breeder's Gazette* and the "Theesarius." Most of my time was given over to tinkering with the Oliver and looking after Bolsich.

In that fruit cake of a prison camp, Bolsich seemed at first to be only a trifle eccentric. After I got to know him, however, I came to realize that he was actually disgusting beyond words. Aside from his principle habit, he also snorted, snuffled, and drooled. His features were oddly puckered, as though he were a canine Mongoloid. The net effect was so stupefyingly loathsome, in fact, that I used to sit there most of the day feeling sorry for the poor brute. I made an honest effort to find good points in his character — and when I finally came to comparing him favorably

199

with Old Jay Dee on the other side of the office, I was well on my way to trouble.

Prowling through the file cabinet one particularly dull afternoon, I came across a set of civil-service-examination papers for the position of prison-camp foreman. It struck me all of a sudden that if Bolsich could compare with the Captain, he should certainly qualify as a foreman. So I amused myself for the remainder of the afternoon by writing that exam in the name of one Jay Dee Bolsich.

It was a foolish thing to do, really, but I had become rather careless, with my feet out of the mud. And after seven months in that camp I had lost a good deal of perspective — especially after writing all those unreadable letters for the Captain. I was almost convinced that I was the only literate in southern Georgia. But I did it up all the way. I hung the Captain's initials on poor, pitiful Bolsich, and made him out the hottest foreman prospect within 1,000 square miles of turpentine country. Then, to milk it for the last chuckle, I mailed the thing. Like an idiot!

Five weeks later, Old Jay Dee received an official envelope from the civil service people. J. D. Bolsich was appointed as a foreman under the Captain's command.

It was hard to tell when the Captain was mad, since he was never really happy and there wasn't much room for comparison. I did, however, detect an extra hardness in his eyes and a certain tightness in his voice when he put down the envelope and began bellowing at me. There was nothing to do but stand there and try to look as humble and contrite as possible, while his blasts of profanity whistled about my ears. After he ran out of swear words, he lapsed into a long rambling discourse on the South and its glories, and the generosity and rare sensitivity of its inhabitants, and why the hell didn't I stay up north instead of coming

200

down here and corrupting their institutions and debauching southern womanhood. He stood fuming, with his chin and his gut out, his hands thrust deep in his greasy pockets.

Finally, Old Jay Dee went completely speechless on me. But he was smiling when he motioned a couple of bulls over and pointed toward the sweatbox. That's the way his sense of humor was.

The sweatbox was a sort of cell, four feet wide by four feet high, and 12 feet long. One side formed a common wall with the kennels for the camp dogs. It was too low to stand up and too narrow to stretch out crosswise. From one end to the other, it was marked off at three-foot intervals with two-by-six framing members that extended across the floor. There was a very faint light that filtered through the cracks in the kennel wall, bringing with it the overpowering odor of a decade's accumulation of dog excreta. The dogs often relieved themselves directly against that sieve of a wall. They also provided a continual medley of sounds, with their yelping and snoring and scratching and copulating.

The sweatbox was mostly used for punishment.

When the two bulls threw me into this haven, I couldn't see a thing. I huddled near the heavy door, thinking obscene thoughts about the Captain and wishing I could go back out and pull pine stumps. Then my eyes became accustomed to the gloom and a lump of pure relief rose in my throat — I wasn't alone in that terrible place. Over in the corner I could see the dim bulk of a fellow prisoner, another member of our great classless mass, a fellow sufferer, united beneath the yoke of our common bondage. He stirred in the darkness and turned to me, doubtless eager for companionship in this dungeon, anxious to hear the voice of another human being.

"What they put y'all in hyah fo?" he asked.

201

"The Cap thinks I'm a baby raper, corrupting your southern women," quipped I in a friendly spirit.

Some place in the darkness I could hear him spit. "No-good, smartass Yankee trash!"

Then he rolled over and went back to sleep.

CHAPTER SIXTEEN

My friend Clyde used to have a little saying that I found cause to remember all too frequently after I finished my sentence in Georgia. "Lordy Lord, O my, O me," ran his lament. "Look where my hard head has caused my poor ass to be."

The freedom that I enjoyed — a bit too thoroughly, perhaps — between the time of my release and my re-incarceration in a Florida jail lasted exactly 15 days. It was the briefest period of freedom in my entire career. I would attribute that mainly to overenthusiasm. All during those long months in the swamp, and especially during my time in the sweatbox, I had been building golden dreams of how things could have been if Marlene and I had been able to pull off our magnificent score and make it to Florida. I kept thinking of those beaches, and of all the shining summer days I would spend on them when I was released.

But, thanks to my hard head, I ended up spending many days in the Palm Beach County Court that summer, while my attorneys haggled over my freedom. Through my own carelessness, I had gotten pinched for defrauding a wealthy West Palm widow out of a great deal of money. The law had landed me without any trouble, but they hadn't been able to fish up so much as a dime of the widow's cash. That omission had everyone particularly upset. The police, the insurance people, and the widow woman all wanted that money. And I wanted my freedom.

A situation like this is tailor-made for dealing. It is the backbone of American justice. It doesn't matter if you've killed your kindly old parents, robbed the orphans' fund, or criminally molested an entire Sunday School class; if you have something to deal with, you can disentangle yourself from the law without earning a single gray hair behind bars.

The most basic form of the deal is to trade a confession for a lesser charge or a lighter sentence. This is classically known as copping a plea. It comes into play when a chap is nailed for, say, rape. The police know he did it, the victim knows it, he knows it; there is not one bit of doubt about it. But the prosecutor is not *sure* that he can secure a conviction, and failure to do so would look bad for everyone. So a deal is made. The fellow pleads guilty to disorderly conduct and is given probation or a suspended jail sentence. Everyone is happy. The police have solved a crime, the criminal has his freedom, the judge has a clean docket and can go fishing, the prosecutor has another conviction to his credit, and the victim is awarded a new cherry. A beautiful system.

There are many variations. If you've been paying off the cops, the deal is obvious; everybody just keeps quiet. Or you can turn informer. In some cases, one party to a murder will be given his freedom in exchange for his testimony. A man can often assure his freedom by giving information about other crimes that he has knowledge of. And if he has an agile enough mind, although lacking definite knowledge, he can even implicate an innocent person in a crime he has only read about in the papers. The whole thing is marvellously flexible.

My variation, in this case, was a very common one. I would trade a sizable, unrecovered lump of loot for my freedom. But deals take time and, with the money still missing, no one was going to be stupid enough to give me a bond. I spent several months in jail while everyone concerned took turns browbeating the judge into the wisdom of allowing such a trade to be effected.

While waiting for wisdom to prevail, I was regularly hauled from jail to court with my fellow recalcitrants, sometimes as frequently as five days a week. My case was usually first on the docket, and my attorneys would immediately plead, motion, and frantically waive — at the judge, at each other, at attractive girls in print dresses, and at the proceedings in general. The prosecutor, who was in no way interested in bringing the action to trial, would agree almost gratefully to put it off. My feelings on the matter were clear to everyone; if I went to prison; they could kiss their chances farewell of ever seeing any of that money.

Each day, the judge would stoically postpone my case and get down to the business at hand. But I couldn't go back to jail until the rest of the prisoners were taken back, so I had no choice but to stick around and find what amusement I could in the circus of courtroom activity. I must have sat through more than 300 cases — a Chinaman charged with assault for cutting off all his wife's hair, motive never determined; a one-armed man up for picking a pocket; a policeman on a morals rap; a hooker pinched for soliciting in a house of worship; a young punk who had

205

swiped a load of tomatoes; a man with a respectable record as a burglar who had been caught poaching alligators, of all things. There were some of the damnedest charges and allegations in that courtroom that I'd ever heard in my life. But they didn't surprise me.

Without half putting his mind to it, a thief can get himself arrested on some pretty screwy charges. Like the time a buddy of mine got pinched with a bottle of nitroglycerin. He was in a dry county down South, and the head hillbilly in the courthouse didn't even care about the explosive — all he was upset about was that the nitro was in a half-pint bottle, and there was a local ordinance against half-pint bottles no matter what they contained. Gave him 30 and 30 for the bottle and poured the soup out of the courthouse window as if it were no more than a bucket of slops. Thirty days in the pokey and 30 days on the road; and after the insanity in that courthouse, which, by the grace of God, was still standing, my friend was tickled pink to have it.

It was while idling away my days in court that I met my first Cubans. The western side of Palm Beach County is well inland, and much of it is devoted to agriculture. The main crop is sugar cane, a type of vegetation that responds especially well to the ministrations of Cubans. There were many, at that time, ministering to the crops, and a large number of them were turning up regularly in the county court, usually on charges of Drunk and Disorderly. D & D is a charge I always resented, because it tends to make a person out a slob, which was definitely not the case with the Cubans. They worked many long hours in the fields for wages that wouldn't have supported a dieting sparrow. And every time they took a few drinks or indulged themselves in a little friendly scuffling, which was about the only entertainment they could afford, the cracker cops hauled them in and whacked them with a fine.

I had two or three of these people with me in the court-house bullpen every court day. This was a small detention cell just off the rear of the courtroom, where prisoners were kept until their cases could be heard. There was a barred window in the door through which we could follow the pro-ceedings, and it often fell my duty to explain the finer points of American justice to my new Latin friends. Having la-bored many years at home for United Fruit before getting hung up in our cane fields, they didn't find the inconsist-encies at all surprising.

One of the Cubans I met during the time I served in the courthouse was a girl named Juanita. She was slim and shapely and attractive, as are most Cuban girls before their first pregnancy, but she had the personality of a truck driver. As a matter of fact, that was what she was charged with. She stood accused of having stolen a pickup truck from one Morgan Carstairs, son of a wealthy Florida farmer. Young Morgan had had his way with her, and then tried to dump her back on the market, as he was reputed to have done already with countless cracker girls. But Jua-nita wouldn't go for it. She sucker-punched Morgan, took the keys to his truck, and cut out. With Morgan and his buddies in hot pursuit, she drove the truck through a barricade at the foot of a bayside street right into six feet of salt water. Carstairs, Senior, had her arrested for *lèse-majesté*.

With preliminary hearings and all, Juanita spent four days in court. The wife of the head turnkey brought her over every day and parked her in a chair outside the bull pen until her case came up. Perhaps it was because I had once done a brief stint as a truck driver, or maybe because I treated her like a lady, but Juanita and I hit it off very well. She had just enough English and I had just enough Spanish so that we could make ourselves understood, and we talked through the little window for a couple of hours every day. Mostly I talked a lot of trash, trying to line her up for a spot of sexual therapy when I got clear of the law. Juanita, however, talked mostly about "son-a-beech" capitalists and things that smacked of revolution. She was so teed off at land owners, not to mention their gutless offspring, that she wouldn't even have anything to do with her countrymen who furthered the system by working for it. Whenever one of the Cubans in the pen with me tried to speak to her, her standard reply was, "Lacy bom, gat fok!"

Juanita's vocabulary in general would have brought a blush to the stubbly cheeks of a Limehouse fishmonger. Wherever she had learned her smattering of English, it had obviously not been in a convent. When she reached for an expletive or an intensifier she found an obscenity. When she was happy over a small joke, or worried about her day in court, she cussed. And when she really got wound up on something, profanities fell from her lovely lips like prayers at a Black Mass.

The proceedings against Juanita moved very slowly. She balked admirably at every stage, and complicated things further by pretending to know less English than she actually did. She made it very clear that she didn't feel her offense was any sort of a crime against society — and that it was none of the court's Goddamn business. When the judge threatened her with contempt, she feigned total ignorance of the language. And when she was asked a question, she would counter with more questions.

"Eez eet against dee law to dreenk in dees country," she asked, when the judge wanted to know how much alcohol she had consumed.

"No, girl, it's not against the law," he replied.

"Then why hell you ask me for about wheesky?"

Her trial went on in that vein for two hours, until she was prevailed upon, at length, to plead guilty. The judge was so relieved to have done with it that he skipped the usual lecture and gave her 30 days. I'm sure the judge thought he was being lenient, but Juanita did not.

"Hey, *chingado*," she said, "eez eet against dee law in dees country to theenk?"

The judge, who surely understood not one word of Spanish, patiently replied that, no, it was not against the law in this country to think.

"Good!" said Juanita. "Then I theenk you are dirty son-a-beech! I theenk you eat sheet! I theenk you . . ."

"*And* 30 more days," screamed the judge, as the turnkey's wife and two bailiffs hustled Juanita from the courtroom.

It was to Juanita's credit that she picked up another 30 days before they got her out the door. And it was a credit to the judge's 70-year-old constitution that he didn't blow out an artery. The old son-a-beech was so mad he closed the court for two days.

To my everlasting regret, I never did get a chance to take a chomp out of Juanita's toothsome hindquarters. But before she disappeared into the bowels of the county jail to serve out her accumulation of sentences, she gave me something that I considered at the time to be far more valuable — the name of a bar on Flagler Street where I could meet a man who just might be willing to take me on as a paid revolutionary.

The appeal this held for me was irresistible. There was a very real possibility of making a nice lump of change, and there was the opportunity for adventure. I mean real adventure, not just the play-acting at being John Dillinger, or the gentleman thief, but real, honest-to-God intrigue. And that was always my big hang-up. Just give me something with a slap-dash air of romance, with a touch of Errol Flynn and the soldier-of-fortune bit thrown in for seasoning, and I would cheerfully abandon a guaranteed score on a Brinks truck — perhaps because the idea of actually overturning established authority seemed far more satisfying than simply flouting the rules of authority. That went for anybody's authority; the people who made the laws, the people who owned the jails, and those in general who sat on the walls screeching "thou shalt not." I had nothing personal against Batista, but if I could hire myself out as a firebrand to the chaps who wanted to screw him, then that was damn well going to be my new bag.

Shortly after Juanita was packed away in duranceville, the local authorities finally decided that I wasn't going to bounce with the loot until I had some guarantees. So the Christian benevolence of the insurance company won out, and a deal was made. I told my lawyer where he could dig up the money, the court decided I was once again a worthy and respectable citizen, and I was allowed to walk out of the county jail as a free man — albeit with a strong recommendation that I get my thieving Yankee ass the hell out of Florida within one week, else I might find myself with a ten-year sentence for any charge that was handy.

A real lot of soreheads in Florida, I thought. But up them, and up with the revolution.

CHAPTER SEVENTEEN

I felt right at home in the Flagler Street bar. Except for the predominance of Cubans, the cast of characters was almost identical to The Brown Bottle back in Detroit. There were hustling girls in tight skirts, touts from Hialeah, small potatoes hoodlums, and a scattering of faggots. There was even the same drunken wildlife — though in this case it was a monkey rather than a swan. The monkey belonged to the bartender, who had accepted it in lieu of an otherwise un-collectable bar bill. It was one of those wretched, chatter-ing, little spider monkeys, mean as sin; and if you tried to pet him, you were likely to lose a finger. He was so far gone in alcoholism that he had absolutely no coordination. Given a beer bottle with a few drops in the bottom, the monkey would stand on his hind legs and drain the bottle, tilting his head back farther and farther until he finally fell over back-wards. His depth perception wasn't much to speak of, either. With a good load on, the monkey would charge across the floor and attempt to leap up onto the bar, as though he were practicing a Gene Kelly dance routine. Invariably he missed, either striking the front of the bar like a furry cannon ball, or clearing it completely and landing head first in the crushed ice. This usually spared him the trouble of passing out.

When I first made the acquaintance of this beast, it was going by the name of Hernandez. Nobody seemed to know who the original Hernandez had been, or how the monkey had come by the name. Some years later, though, I dropped into the same bar and found that Hernandez was still in residence — only now he was going by the name of Bobby. There was no doubt where this name had come from. It was right after the McClellan hearings, and the regular patrons, who had watched the proceedings on television, had been struck by what they claimed was an exact counterpart of Hernandez' chattering and his puckered features. They had renamed him after Bobby Kennedy.

But Hernandez, and the hustling girls, and the half-witted bartender with the harelip and the colorful backwash of human refuse that would have drawn vacationing garment manufacturers like leeches, if the establishment had been further uptown, all paled to insignificance beside the figure that dominated the entire bar. This was the man Juanita had told me about, the one I had come looking for in my idiot quest for adventure and semi-illegal riches — the notorious Cojones Grandes.

That wasn't his real name, of course. It was a title of respect given to him by his associates, and it meant that he was a most formidable fellow. The same title is current in every jail and prison in the world, where common usage demands that a fellow's courage be equated to the hypothetical size of his testicles. *"Des bons poids,"* or *"couilles comme un boeuf"* in the Marseilles lockups become "balls

212

that won't quit" in Scranton, or "knuckle nuts" in Chicago. Elsewhere, a man with much heart is said to have "melons for cods," while his timid companions have "cods like mustard seeds."

Naturally, my hillbilly friends in Georgia had their own peculiar variation of this equation. It derived from a regional criterion for determining the worth of a bull, only they talked about one end when they really meant the other. If a con threw down his stump axe and told the Captain to shove it, or if the Captain handed him a stump axe and told *him* to shove it, he was sure to be rewarded with the observation, "Man theah sho 'nuff got eyes this far apart!", accompanied by the appropriate gesture of scorn or esteem. For a sniveler, the thumb and forefinger might be pressed tightly together, indicating a degree of chicken-heartedness so extreme that the eyes overlap. But if the hands are held any place from a foot to a yard apart, then that man has *real* balls.

When a man is hefty enough in that department to go by the name of Cojones Grandes, you can generally depend on him being alright. It means that he is not a fink, that he has all the brass parts ever frozen off the proverbial monkey, that he will eat no one's Dreck, and that he is in roughly the same business you are. And he definitely is not a cop. No matter what daring feats of bravery or wit they may aspire to, it's simply impossible for cops or screws to accumulate any appreciable amount of balls.

Cojones Grandes' real name was Jesus Ramirez. There is always the temptation to call that a Christian name, but that would be too obvious, and Cojones was anything but a Christian. He was a hard-eyed, mustachioed man who looked to be a blend of Falstaff and Pancho Villa. He was fat and rumpled in the way that only a fat but active man

213

can be rumpled, with his shirt always untucked at one point or another around his ample perimeter, and a hairy swatch of belly showing through where the buttons had yielded to the internal pressures of two cases of beer per day. When he walked, his huge buttocks were constantly elbowing and jostling each other, barely contained in the army fatigues that made up his entire wardrobe. From behind, he looked like a sack race with saddlebags.

In spite of his bulk and déshabillé, Cojones didn't radiate the usual fat man's aura of slob; nor did he fall back on the corpulent role of clown. He had a rich sense of the absurd, and he laughed at everything from Simon Bolivar to the DAR, but he never felt any false social obligation to laugh at his own bulk. Cojones thought skinny and conducted himself skinny. He pursued his daily course through thickets of bar patrons, bottle-laden tables, buses, crowded supermarkets, turnstiles, alleys too constricted for a pregnant goat, and narrow doorways; mincing along as steadfastly and confidently as a 98-pound broken-field runner, and leaving in his wake an uproar of broken merchandise, stove-in citizens, and bent doorknobs.

He was an educated man, who spoke perfect English and lived according to a strict sense of values. Only one month before achieving a law degree at the University of Michigan he had read off the faculty as a flock of bourgeois reactionaries and packed himself back to Cuba to become a chicken plucker. I never learned the reason for his disaffection with the U of M, but I suspected it had something to do with the debauching of coeds. Once he found out I was familiar with Ann Arbor, he began dropping an occasional lug on the "morals Gestapo," referring to the Campus Police. And if the Falstaffian side of his nature had been as

214

pronounced in middle-class Ann Arbor as it was in the more disreputable quarters of Miami, I could well believe it.

Cojones' life was dedicated to the pursuit of three passions: women, alcohol, and revolutions. He never deviated — unless you want to run a lot of technical orthodoxy about his conduct in bed, and none of his partners ever had anything but praise for that. Women brought joy to his life, alcohol furnished the fuel, and revolution gave him purpose. It was a minor revolution, in fact, that earned Jesus his cojones.

He was working as a chicken plucker at the time, on a small farm 20 miles out of Pinar Del Rio. One afternoon, he and a group of friends were sharing a few gallons of rum in the annex of a nearby distillery. It was a festive little gathering, with peasants passed out on piles of cane, an abundance of wenches, and the plangent discord of drunken guitars. Cojones had temporarily satisfied two of his passions, and was working on the third by treating the distillery workers to a lecture on the unconstitutionality of the Batista regime. This was before Castro's raid on Fort Moncada, and the ensuing trial that made revolution a respectable pastime in Cuba. Consequently, Cojones was not making much of a hit with the crowd. A few timid nods of assent, an occasional waving of the red stocking cap, but no real taste for the barricades. Clearly, the only way to inspire the downtrodden was to perform an act of defiance against the regime. What, though, to defy in the open countryside, midway between a sugar refinery and a chicken ranch?

As Cojones saw it, there was only one course of action. He would personally raid the nearest army garrison. This was a shack of an outpost only half a mile from the distillery. The government was represented there by four ancient soldiers, doddering on the edge of retirement, and a brand new tank that had been donated to Batista by the United States government to help defend the campesinos of the region against the onslaughts of discontent. It was a very beautiful tank, and Cojones knew clear down to his cojones that he had to have it.

With the steely determination of the born guerilla, he set out immediately for his objective, slithering snake-like through the cane field that lay between the distillery and the garrison. His progress through the field was marked by a great threshing and laying waste of sugary stalks that may have cost the land holder a tenth of his crop. But none of the old men on duty at the garrison noticed this carnage. As a gesture of good will and a concession to graft, the neighboring distillery furnished the troops with free rum. The entire garrison was unconscious 23 hours a day.

Unaware of his immunity from detection, Cojones approached the tank with elephantine stealth, kicking over a pile of crates and sending terrified chickens squawking in all directions. Climbing into a tank can be an awkward maneuver even when the climber is sober and genuinely agile. For a 240-pound revolutionary with close to a quart of day-old rum in his paunch, it should have been impossible. But the more he drinks the thinner he thinks, and at two quarts Cojones would not balk at trying to thread a gopher hole. He went through the hatch headfirst, and by the time he'd flailed and floundered his way into the driver's seat, he had already punched enough buttons to have the engine turning over.

Without awakening the garrison, Cojones put the tank in gear and drove it neatly through one corner of the headquarters shack. He then aimed it roughly in the direction of the distillery, which took him back into the cane field. Once surrounded by the tall stalks, he lost all sense of direction and spent nearly 20 minutes roaring through the field at full speed, describing immense loops, circles, and figure eights; in the process, churning the field into a huge, sweet salad.

This entire performance had been witnessed by the celebrants back at the distillery. From the apparent slaughter of the garrison to the systematic destruction of the absentee landlord's crop, they had looked on with a mixture of awe and admiration. Some were so awed that they set aside their rum and ran like hell. But the others were on hand to cheer when Cojones found his way out of the field and stalled the tank two feet short of the distillery. Cojones had won his first converts.

His revolution, however, was probably the most aimless on record. While Cojones remained inside the tank accepting libations through the hatch and explaining the mysteries of heavy armor to a brace of young ladies, his friends painted the tank with such fiery slogans as *Liberdad* and *Viva la Revoluçion*. Then, after taking aboard a further consignment of rum and upwards of a dozen student revolutionaries, including two guitarists and a ten-year-old bongo player who doubled on marachas, Cojones set out on a triumphal tour of the area. If he and his group lacked specific goals, they did not lack enthusiasm. Before the tank ran out of fuel four hours later, the rebel band had decimated 1,000 acres of cane and had treated the rural population to the bawdiest and longest rendition of *La Cucaracha* ever heard in that province. They also succeeded in firing three shells from the tank's cannon before a casing became inextricably jammed in the breech. The first shell inflicted only minor damage to the distillery, although causing its total evacuation; the second wiped out

217

a pine tree, while the third demolished a privy that had survived the Spanish-American War and two subsequent uprisings.

Although the Cojones Rebellion accomplished no discernible purpose, it did make a lasting impression in many quarters. When the locals finally came out of their hidey holes, they all agreed that Jesus Ramirez was an *hombre con cojones muy grandes*. And Batista must have agreed with them, because he immediately slapped a $1,000 reward on Cojones' head.

That reward, as Cojones would point out at the smallest provocation, was never lifted. Even when the Batista government was handing out amnesties to Castro and his raiders like bibs at a kindergarten picnic, Cojones was still officially regarded as a serious threat to the Establishment, and as an agitator of no small cojones.

If there was one thing that Cojones had more of than he did cojones, it was money. He produced it in thick wads from the side pockets of his fatigue pants, paying for drinks, disbursing funds to dark, mysterious-looking Cubans who nodded and smiled and went their strange little ways never to be seen again, and stuffing bills down the blouses and up the skirts of laughing girls. Since Cojones never worked, the source of his income was often a subject of speculation. When asked about it directly, he would smile and mumble something vague about a Ford Fellowship or a grant from the Guggenheim Foundation for a treatise he was preparing on the Statutes and Torts of the Jivaro head-hunters; a palpable fiction that didn't deceive me for a single moment.

Sources of money have always held a great fascination for me, so I watched and listened and pieced together small bits of information, and by the time Cojones trusted me enough to hint at the details, I already knew most of the

218

story. His money was coming from two sources; a Cuban national, and an American who smelled like an F.B.I. man. The Cuban, it turned out, was a fellow named Pedro Miret who had done time in a Mexican prison for transporting illegal arms. With a Mexican parole fresh in his pocket, he was now heading up the Cuban Committee in Exile, raising money for weapons and supplies, and doling it out to men like Cojones, the foremen of the revolutionary shop.

The F.B.I. type went by the name of Mendosa, even though his hair was almost white and his eyes were the palest of blue. According to Cojones, Mendosa was with the Central Intelligence Agency. This seemed somewhat improbable, inasmuch as our government was openly supporting Batista's dictatorship, but Cojones claimed that the CIA was interested in buying a share of the Castro organization just in case our military advisers and arms shipments to Batista proved ineffective in suppressing the revolution. However much truth there may have been in this, Cojones remained loyal to his principles. He conscientiously spent every cent of Miret's money on arms and supplies. Mendosa's went for alcohol and young ladies.

It was while sucking up some of Mendosa's money that Cojones first introduced me to a fellow who seemed to be as strung out on the glamor and romance of it all as I was. We were probably both a little simple in the head, and I'm sure we were a great source of amusement to Cojones, but with our identically parallel enthusiasms it was only natural that we thought each other the sharpest chaps ever to enlist in the noble and profitable cause of national revolution.

Hercules Renaud, the son of a Martinique civil servant, had gone after the same things in life that I had, in much the same way. His father had sent him to school in France and that hadn't worked out very well, because Hercules

219

had only rattled around among a dozen or so lycées and had finally gotten himself drummed out of the Sorbonne. From there he had drifted into the rackets and in and out of three prisons before deciding to bug out for a fresh go at it.

In Florida he found everything he needed — a Jesus haircut and a close-cropped beard that made him look a bit like Paul of Tarsas — and good old game-for-anything me.

Anxious to get started in the revolutionary business, Hercules and I went with Cojones one night to help unload guns. The unloading at that time was being done at an old shed a few miles up the Miami River. The guns were purchased from illegal sources and held at the shed until Cojones could arrange for a boat to transport them to the island. Too many people already knew about that shed, but I wasn't aware of it and neither was Herky. For us, it was too much like something out of a Humphrey Bogart movie to be anything but pure glamor — the bright moonlight shining down on the rutted little road that led off through the swamp, the half-dozen Cubans huddled silently against the night's chill, the waiting and the feeling of danger. Now and then, the Cubans would talk quietly among themselves, and one of them would wander up toward the highway for a look around. Wonderful! Orson Welles never had a supporting cast that perfect. We even had a beautiful and darkly mysterious woman along — at least she would have been mysterious if I hadn't known she was a waitress in one of the Cuban restaurants in Miami. Anyway, Cojones had her in the back room of the shed, so she didn't really count.

After a two-hour wait, the truck finally came; a large van with no headlights showing. Herky and I and the six Cubans began pulling the stuff out and hauling it into the shed.

220

There were many wooden boxes of ammunition, two crates of rifles, and some wicked-looking machineguns and other weapons that only had a tarpaulin thrown over them. All of it was heavier than hell.

We had half the stuff off the truck when we found out about the U.S. marshals. Apparently they had been waiting all evening in the thicket, just a few feet away from us, because they suddenly came charging in at us from all directions. Every place I looked there was a flashlight with a voice behind it yelling for everybody to stay right where they were. Nobody did.

Herky immediately dropped his end of the crate we were carrying and headed for the river. His presence of mind almost cost me a broken toe, but I didn't even notice it at that time. I spotted a gap in the surrounding flashlights and ran like hell for it, angling off in the general direction of Miami or New York, all depending on how soon my wind gave out.

I was making very good time, and had left the uproar of the raid far behind, when I suddenly became aware of a monstrous smashing in the palmetto thicket behind me. It sounded exactly like the fuzz coming through there with a squad car. Back in a couple of my high schools, I had been considered a pretty swift fellow on the track teams, and when I heard the sounds of pursuit I poured on the speed as though I were still running the four-forty against invincible Ypsi High. But I knew I was losing ground.

A moment later, I heard a voice right behind me: "Man, you are a running son-of-a-bitch!"

I looked around, and it was Cojones. He was carrying a Browning Automatic Rifle on each shoulder, and he was dressed in nothing but a contraceptive. He billowed past me as though I were going the other way, toward the Gulf.

221

"Hey hey, John boy," he sang out in passing. "Just like the arboretum, no? You ever have to make it out of there with the beer on your back and the A-square feds on your tail?"

And then he was gone in a cloud of buttocks. Man, he sure could run!

It has been one of the little tragedies of my life that few of my hare-brained fantasies have ever taken substance with all of the frills and furbelows intact. What I was looking for when I engaged myself with the Flagler Street bunch was plain, raw adventure — not a job as a stevedore with aspirations to becoming a track star. I knew very clearly that I wasn't cut out to be a flunky, or to stand on street corners passing out inflammatory literature, or to settle for leftovers from the backroom of some penny ante anarchist.

I was glooming over this a couple of days after the big munitions raid when Herky showed up at the bar with a small, weasely individual named Henry VanCleef. He was the owner of a prosperous Miami real estate company, and instead of devoting his money and his leisure to the more sensible pursuit of women, or the more common southern pursuit of evangelism, he affected a deep interest in international politics. Henry was sincere. He thought Batista was the dirtiest bastard who ever trod down on a peasant, and he just knew that, with a bit of help from dedicated people such as he, everything was going to work out fine and dandy for the little folks. Sure. In spite of his money and his $200 silk suits, Henry was still a hillbilly with the sort of confidence in the equity of those cosmic balance scales that is only found in people from south of the Mason-Dixon line or west of the Mississippi.

And Henry, in his pinched little way, was hot for adventure. He had a friend, he explained, who owned a 42-foot

222

cabin cruiser. It was their unswervable ambition to go to the aid of Fidel Castro, uplifter of the sagging *campesinos*; and if we could line up a cargo and the necessary contacts at the Cuban end, he and his yachtsman buddy would supply the transportation. A real swinging deal if there ever was one, thought I.

While Herky closeted himself with Cojones and outlined the scheme to him, I plied Henry with drink and tried to learn a few details about his friend. From what I could make out, the fellow had been born and raised in Phoenix. He'd had the cabin cruiser — the first boat he'd ever set foot on — for all of one week, having purchased it for the bargain price of $7,500. Somehow, that didn't sound too promising. But when Herky came back, he whispered in my ear that Cojones would furnish the cargo and pay the two of us $300 apiece to haul it to Cuba. Henry and friend would be remunerated with all the glory and self-satisfaction they could absorb.

That sounded unethical enough to appeal beautifully to my baser instincts. So we piled Henry into a cab and headed for the Miami River to have a look at our transportation.

From 100 yards down the waterfront, the boat didn't look so bad. In fact, it looked pretty much like all the other pleasure craft moored in those waters — snowy-white topsides and gleaming mahogany. But, from a distance, all boats fall into a single generic lump of hull and luxury. And that would be fine if you could only sail the damn things from 100 yards away. It's only when you get within practical eyeball range, though, that a boat reveals itself as the cranky and highly individual article that it is. With the enchantment of distance, this one was a real beauty, a well kept matron from a bygone day of yachting. And the two figures waving to us from the deck might have been a cou-

223

ple of millionaires ready for an afternoon of highballs and sailfish.

The enchantment faded quickly as we drew nearer. Those snowy topsides were chewed and scruffy from years of intimacy with abrasive docks. The gleaming mahogany was swollen and split with dry rot. And if there was any trace of a water line painted on that hull, it was someplace beneath the surface of the Miami River. As this seedy and dissipated craft rocked mournfully in the sun, I caught a prophetic glimpse of the name printed across its transom in faded gold leaf — *Mary Celeste II.*

I've never put much stock in burning bushes, but that was enough for me. I did an abrupt about-face and would have been halfway back to Flagler Street, or even Woodward Avenue, if Herky hadn't snatched me by the shirttail.

"Hold on, John," said he. "Give it a chance. Just think of the pure, beautiful adventure; the sparkling waves; the tropic nights on the Caribbean; the money."

"Yeah," said I, with a rare burst of clarity, "getting caught by the first guy from the Coast Guard who knows how to dog paddle; Hurricane Carol; the bottom of the Caribbean; 300 lousy bucks."

But reality can be such a bore — so I followed Henry and Herky on board and met the "millionaires," who turned out to be even scruffier than the boat. The owner of the boat was a twin sister to Henry, a smarmy and dedicated weasel with the sort of pencil-line mustache I always associated with pimps, even though few of them ever wore the things. His name was Jerry, and he was the kind of creep who wanted you to run around calling him "Skipper." In a pig's valise I would call him Skipper. Two minutes of conversation convinced me that this idiot couldn't have found a berth in a maternity ward, and the only consideration that

224

kept me from slinging his dumb ass into the river was the fact that he owned the boat.

The second millionaire, and the fifth member of our little crew, was a mean-looking old man with his shirt collar turned up and his yachting cap pulled down over his eyes in a singularly sinister manner, as though he were saying all the time, "Get smart with me, punk, and I'll beat you into a jellied mackerel." He was standing by the helm, conning the river in both directions out of the corners of his eyes.

"Who's the mean-looking old man," I asked Jerry.

As soon as I mentioned him, the old man stepped away from the helm. "Get smart with me, punk," he said, "and I'll beat you into a jellied mackerel. My name's Coley Johnson."

Coley Johnson was not exactly a stranger to me. I'd seen him a few times around Detroit, and I'd heard quite a few stories about him. He had made himself locally famous during Prohibition with his unorthodox — and generally unsuccessful — schemes for bringing vast quantities of tipple into the country. Once he had planned to steal a huge excursion boat that made daily runs to Boblo Island and use it to hijack the entire contents of a Canadian distillery. He eventually compromised and located a 100-foot steam yacht instead, but he ran into a small problem with the crew — he couldn't find one single hood with enough confidence in either his leadership or his seamanship to go along with him. So Coley resorted to the most direct approach he could think of. He took a submachine gun around to Cullinan's Chowder and Oyster Emporium and shanghaied a floating crap game.

Before the dice even had a chance to cool, Coley had the boys on board the steam yacht, shoveling coal and casting off lines. And except for the boat sinking when he ran it

225

into an abutment of the Ambassador Bridge, he almost made it to Canada. Put Coley's brains in a jaybird, the boys used to say, and the son-of-a-bitch would fly backwards.

Our first difficulties arose over the rat. I've never been particularly fond of the beasts, but after sharing innumerable cells with them I had learned that they generally won't bother you if you don't bother them. And, aside from that one exception, they have much in common with people. They just scuffle for their goodies like anyone else, and try to make it without getting tromped on too heavily. This particular specimen, unfortunately, was doing his scuffling on the wrong craft.

We discovered our rat was on board shortly after we cleared Biscayne Bay. I was lounging in the stern, enjoying a bottle of beer and watching the graceful, looping curves of the wake that marked our unseamanlike progress from Miami, when Henry came bursting up out of the cabin.

"There's a rat down there!" he screeched, like he'd just found a water buffalo mucking about in the bilges.

That set Jerry off. "Kill it!" he screamed. "Kill it! I won't have a rat on any Goddamn ship of mine. Over the side with the son-of-a-bitch!"

Since Henry showed little inclination to return to a cabin that was being infested by a rat, Herky and Coley and I decided to pool our strength and our wits to clear the ship of vermin. Arming ourselves with such handy weapons as old deck shoes, a length of rope, a boat hook, and a gaff, we descended into the cabin and deployed along the aft bulkhead. The rat was on a bookshelf at the forward end of the cabin. He was seated on his haunches, thoughtfully chewing on an O Henry candy bar, and he didn't even trouble himself to look up when we came in.

226

"Well, screw me for a chorus girl," said Coley, "if that dirty bastard ain't woofin' up my sea rations." So saying, he took a choke-up grip halfway along the boat hook and loosed a mighty swing at the rat. The bronze tip of the hook slashed a vicious arc that ended just under Herky's left ear, neatly laying him out on the deck.

As a wee lad back in Detroit, I had been recognized as one of the foremost rock pitchers on the east side. And, with all due modesty, I can say that no street light had been beyond the reach of my deadly aim. I now brought this same skill into play once again and let fly with a deck shoe. If the rat had remained decently still instead of running around in a panic, I'm sure I would have had him. Thanks to my early training, however, I got nothing more than a cabin light. Figuring I could get another shot at the rat if he came out from behind the books at the far end of the shelf, I leaped for the starboard side of the cabin — but found myself blocked by Herky, who was crawling about on the deck and impolitely questioning Coley's antecedents.

I dropped down beside Herky just as Coley took another swipe with the boat hook. This time he knocked all the books off the shelf and shattered a full bottle of rum. Stripped of his shelter, the rat scrambled along the wooden molding beneath the cabin windows and dove through a crack behind the starboard bunk. During this quick transit, Coley made two attempts to spear the beast with the boat hook, taking out two more windows in the process.

"Wait a minute!" I yelled, as I managed to get a death grip on the butt end of the madly flailing boat hook. "Just hold on there, Coley, before you knock the damn boat all to hell. We've got him cornered now. All we have to do is outthink him."

227

"Yeah," said Coley, slapping a heavy volume of Bowditch over the crack behind the bunk. "Ain't no way in hell he can get away now."

Coley relinquished his grip on the boat hook and sat down on the deck with Herky and me while we planned our next move. The bunk, so called, was little more than five feet long. It was blocked in all the way around — the hull on the far side, the aft bulkhead at one end, a chart table at the other, and a sliding door on what would have been the open side so that gear could be stowed beneath it. With Bowditch holding down the original point of entry, and disregarding the possibility of further cracks and crevices, the rat was theoretically trapped.

With the situation more clearly defined, I motioned the others aside and selected weapons suitable to the terrain — a flashlight and the fish gaff. I also had enough foresight to put on a pair of heavy canvas gloves generally used for handling anchors and engine parts. A cornered rat, given half an opportunity, will take your finger off clear up to the elbow.

Thus equipped, I got down on all fours, slid the door aside, and shined the light inside. Far back in the corner, two mean and beady points of light glared back at me. The dirty rat was cowering behind one of the hull frames, and when I poked tentatively in its direction with the gaff, it screeched like a fiend incarnate. I jabbed at it a couple more times, but only succeeded in driving it farther back in its refuge. Finally, I took a powerful swing with the gaff and felt the point sink deeply into something soft and yielding. Ah, you little swine, thought I — I have you now.

Thinking to dislodge the unwholesome corpse of my adversary from its hiding place, I gave the handle of the gaff a strong tug. I was rewarded with a sound of ripping and

228

splintering wood that fair stood my hair on end. Letting go of the gaff, I thrust the flashlight back under the bunk to see what had happened.

The point of the gaff had struck dry rot in the framing member, and I had pulled a foot-long section of it entirely free of the hull — complete with the nails that had originally secured the planking to the frame. Water, in an all too generous quantity, seemed to be entering our boat through the holes left by these nails.

The leak, as it turned out, amounted to no more than a trifling 12 gallons an hour. Herky felt certain he could reduce it to three or four by climbing over the side and nailing a piece of canvas over the damaged section of hull, but I wasn't much enchanted by the idea of doing any hammering on that rotten hull. I talked him out of his notion, not by convincing him of the danger to the hull, but by pointing out the huge number of uncooked fish swimming hungrily around our boat. Herky decided not to go over the side, and we found that we could handle the leak nicely by taking turns on the ancient bilge pump.

Except for the rat, the trip down was uneventful, and our ship's log would have been dull reading — if any of us had been salty enough to keep a log. But logs are only glorified diaries, so to hell with it, we said. In due course, we made our unlogged landfall at Punta Maisi, the easternmost tip of Cuba, and altered course to head the boat into the Windward Passage between Cuba and Hispaniola. Did it very smartly, too — with only one false start toward the open Atlantic when Coley disagreed with Henry on the relative positions of port and starboard. Somehow, Coley had starboard associated with "the morning star," and to him the term always meant East.

That evening we dropped anchor just off the Oriente

229

coastline, about even with Pico Turquino. The sea was dead, and flat as a tub of bathwater, and the air was perfectly still. From onshore we could hear birds squawking and haggling in the thick undergrowth. And from one of the three other boats that were cruising those same waters a mile or so from shore we could hear the lovely strains of *Luna Rosa*, crackling from the loudspeaker of a phonograph. Such were the mysterious dangers of the smuggling business.

In keeping with the instructions we had from Cojones, we waited until 11:00 P.M., and then began flashing a recognition signal toward shore at five-minute intervals. Simultaneously, the three boats farther out began blinking their lights in colorful patterns, . . . and four more points of light began blinking merrily away from different points along the coast. It looked like a flashlight convention, and it would have taken a couple of computers to make any sense out of the hodgepodge of signals being reflected off the water and intermittently obscured by foliage.

No one else seemed to be paying any attention to the five-minute interval thing, so Herky climbed up on the cabin roof and began blinking out steady signals: three long, two short, over and over. At 11:15 P.M., an airplane came in low overhead from the general direction of Manzanillo and everybody stopped signaling, but not for long. Before the plane's running lights were a mile beyond us, everyone went back to twinkling and flashing with undiminished enthusiasm.

A half-hour later we could hear boats putting out from shore, and within a few minutes one of them was alongside. As soon as the boat scraped against our hull, a man stood up in the bow and shined a powerful lamp in my eyes — three long and two short. No doubt about it, this was our rendezvous.

230

CHAPTER EIGHTEEN

Things have a lovely way of falling apart just about the time they're beginning to look good. You grunt and shove and grind and flail about — and as soon as you have it in the bag, the whole damn bag splits wide open. Take that leak, for instance. It was our one, biggest problem in getting the load of guns to Cuba. And it was nothing. We took turns on the pump going down. There was always one of us sloshing away at it even while the guns were being unloaded off Oriente. And by the time we put about and headed back toward Florida, minus our heavy cargo, the stints on the pump had become an invigorating routine. The other, lesser problems — crew incompatibility, mutinous rats, inexperience, idiot idealism, and failure to recognize the impossibility of our venture — had been blithely disregarded and easily overcome. We felt justifiably proud of ourselves. And as we rolled home o'er the foam-flecked main, we voiced our satisfaction in many a sprightly chanty.

Then the Goddamn bag broke.

We were cruising exuberantly at full throttle past An-
dros Island, when it became abruptly obvious to even the
most starry-eyed among us that our venture had gone
aground. Literally.

Striking a coral head at 15 knots is much the same as
driving into a brick wall at 30 miles an hour — with the
single, significant exception that an automobile will remain
on the surface of the road. When Coley ran us onto the reef
right in the middle of Herky's rendition of "Haul Away
Lads, Haul Away Home," the *Mary Celeste II* instantly
lost all forward motion. Not so the crew. Herky flew from
the cabin roof, bounced twice on the foredeck, and shot
straight out over the bow as though he'd been launched
from a torpedo tube. VanCleef and Jerry smashed through
the cabin door and landed in a tangle against the forward
bulkhead. I wound up half overboard, astraddle of a stan-
chion that had torn loose from the combing. And Coley,
who had succeeded in hanging onto the helm, appeared
only to have flipped a little farther out.

"Avast, there," he was screaming. "Man the pump,
matey. Back and fill, I say. Fetch me Miss Edwiner and
sail my ship for the Panamar!"

Avast, my ass. The boat was sinking, and this super-
annuated Al Capone was playing Blackbeard. I took one
look to make sure everyone was halfway alright, then
dropped over the side. By the time the Atlantic Ocean was
splashing around Coley's boney ankles, I was already halfway to shore.

Once we were all safe on dry land and had convinced the
authorities that we were nothing more than an innocent
group of castaway sports fishermen, Herky and I held a
meeting. We decided that VanCleef and Jerry and Coley
were just plainly too stupid to drool and that we would be

232

somewhat better off without their association. So the five of us parted company. We caught a conch boat to Nassau, and our three disaffiliated members took the first plane out for Miami. Herky took the second, promising to find another boat after picking up our money from Cojones and arranging for a new shipment of arms.

By this time, I was losing my initial enthusiasm for our venture, so I was more than content to remain behind, recuperating from the terrors of my near-drowning in the cause of the revolution, languishing on the beach, and trying to go broke on dollar-a-gallon rum.

Three weeks later, Hercules came back with a 46-foot ketch and three new crew members; a Cuban, who really wanted to help Castro for patriotic reasons and who would lend our enterprise a legitimate flavor in the event we were caught, a guy named O'Hara, who was wanted in Georgia for armed robbery, and a fat, borderline moron, who would be stupid enough to take the rap for the ketch — which had been stolen from a dock in the Miami Municipal Yacht Basin.

Since the boat was practically hot enough to boil the water it sailed in, we also had new instructions. Instead of making delivery to Cuba as before, we were to sail across the Gulf of Mexico and deliver our cargo of Browning Automatic Rifles at a place on the Tuxpan River, which was being used as a staging area for Cuban infiltrators.

We never got there. Two days out from the nearest Mexican landfall, the Caribbean treated us to one of its nastier storms. Twenty knots of wind would have been sufficient to terrify anyone in that crew, lubbers that we were, but the gales that swept down on us for the next 24 hours, and the waves that towered 20 feet above our decks, put us into a virtual state of shock. Before taking refuge in the cabin and

233

lapsing into total paralysis, Herky and I managed to rig storm sails in place of the main and mizzen that had blown themselves to tatters at the first hint of a blow. Then there was nothing to do but wedge ourselves into the bunks while the boat stood first on one end, then on the other, groaning and shuddering and screeching in its timbers until there was no doubt in any of us that it would be torn completely apart the next time it buried its bow in a wave.

Herky rode it out nipping on a bottle of bourbon. I stayed sober and cursed the stupidity that had gotten me into this mess in the first place. Our three shipmates were messily seasick all through the storm, with O'Hara spending a lot of time on his knees promising J. Edgar Hoover, God, and other influential people that he'd never do it again if only the storm would go away.

A couple of years later, the storm did go away; the wind died away to nothing, and the waves subsided, leaving the boat wallowing horribly and rattling worse than ever. Far-off in the distance, we could see the Mexican coast. This occasioned great rejoicing, in spite of the fact that two or three more hours of storm would have blown us straight onto the shore and undoubtedly killed the lot of us. By carefully checking the scanty charts furnished by the previous owner, we determined that we were about ten miles distant from a small port by the name of Alvarado. This was only something like 200 miles off course, but it had the virtue of being on dry land, so we started the water-clogged auxiliary engine with considerable difficulty and headed for shore without delay.

It was well after dark when we reached the harbor and killed the engine alongside a rickety wharf. Herky and I were hard put to restrain our crew from scrambling ashore immediately, but by dint of much cursing and kicking we convinced them of the need for securing the ship. We hunted through lockers and dug beneath piles of wet canvas, looking for anchor chains and mooring lines. After half an hour of rooting and clambering around in the dark, we had our stern tied to a fishing boat and our bow neatly jammed between the pilings of the wharf. With this accomplished, everyone promptly abandoned ship. Everyone but me. I was too exhausted to do anything more than climb into a wet bunk and pass out.

At five o'clock the next morning I was rudely jolted from my bunk. I came suddenly awake when I hit the deck in a tangle of bedding and anchor chain that we had left unstowed from the night before. At first I thought we had run onto another reef, and I was already clawing beneath the bunk for a life preserver before it occurred to me that we were snugly at anchor and safe from navigational hazards. Perhaps we had been rammed by one of the fishing boats. I untangled myself from the blankets, ready to go on deck and raise hell with whoever was banging up our topsides, and found myself surrounded by four Mexicans in the olive-colored uniforms of the Federal Police.

"Well, hi there," I said. "What can I do for you fellows?"

"Seet on bonk and say nothings," said one of the four, pointing a very large revolver in my direction.

I sat on the bonk and said nothings while the other three cops set about shaking down the cabin. I could see that the other bunk hadn't been slept in, so apparently Herky had found himself a señorita and stayed ashore overnight. The rest of the crew, of course, was still suffering from seasickness, and it was no surprise that they hadn't returned to the boat. Until it was actually time to sail, those creeps wouldn't be melted and poured back on board.

It took the cops less than two minutes to turn up the first

235

crate of BARs. They ripped it open, and the officer who seemed to be in charge pulled out one of the guns. He came over and stuck the barrel in my face.

"Gunrunner, eh? You want moch time in preeson, eh? Geeve me your papers, *por favor*."

All I could do was shrug. We had no papers for our stolen boat. And we hadn't figured on needing passports, forged or otherwise, for our smuggling operation.

"Sorry, Pal!" I said, "*no tengo*. I lost 'em overboard."

"Aha! Also illegal entry." He handed the Browning to one of his subordinates and pulled a notebook out of his hip pocket. "Your name, *Señor*, and your country of origin. You will tell me, eh?"

I looked him straight in the eye and smiled sweetly. "I am a Cuban national and my name is Sancho Panza."

The cop was either weak in literature or he just didn't give a good goddamn. Probably both. He wrote down the name without turning a hair, and the name stuck for the rest of the time I was in Mexico. I didn't particularly care whether he believed it or not, because that was the only one he was going to get out of me. It's just good criminal policy never to give your right name. Sometimes the cops are careless and they never get a make on you, which spares you one more arrest on your F.B.I. sheet. Most of the time, of course, they print you and run you through R and I, and all that sort of scientific investigation crap, and find out who you are anyway. They're sporty about it, though, and they always let you keep your phony name as long as they have you in custody. But the police still have their fun by adding a new alias to your sheet. Then they sit around slapping one another on the badge and feeling very clever at having found you out. It's rather like a game, you know.

If you want to be sullen about it, of course, you don't

236

have to give them any name at all. In that case you are booked as John Doe, probably the dullest and the most unimaginative name ever devised. Can you visualize doing a 20-year stretch in the penitentiary under a name like John Doe? I've known a couple of poor slobs who did exactly that. But, as my own F.B.I. sheet will bear out, I've never had to be penalized in that way for refusing to play the game. I've been arrested under aliases ranging from such simple names as John Brodie and Len Irwin to the veritable orgy of a name under which I was once arrested in Montreal — Jacques Henri De La Croix. Between these extremes, and depending upon my mood at the time of the pinch, I have been known as Mortimer Cranbrook, Dion Pfabe, Carson Harson, Clyde Barrow, and Felix Mielzinski. A noble lineage, don't you think? Well, that's nothing. One time in Philadelphia I was successfully arrested as Rupert of Hentzau.

But there *are* rules to the game. My old friend Wimpy once told an Irish desk sergeant that his name was Saint Patrick. But then Wimpy was notorious for such patent stupidities. I had another friend who stood a pinch in Jackson Hole, Wyoming. He made the mistake of telling the cowboy fuzz his real name, which happened to be William Cody. The law kicked him all over the station house like a smartass buffalo before he wised up and decided he'd better cop out to being somebody less historical. So he told them he was Arthur Flegenheimer, and they thought that was just fine and they went ahead and booked him.

After they had rooted out the rest of the guns and ascertained that I had been born in Havana in 1930 under the sign of Scorpio, the head cop and two of his buddies escorted me ashore. One cop remained on board to arrest my confederates when they showed up; a most unlikely eventuality since he was doing his waiting comfortably and conspicuously in the cockpit. When Herky spotted that uniform flaked out on our boat, he would damn sure catch the first anything heading north.

I was lodged in the local jail, a drab building that seemed to have been made over from a cantina. At any rate, there was a bar in the squad room. It was further furnished with an old desk, a bench, a rack of disreputable looking rifles and shotguns — no two of the same manufacture — and a kerosene refrigerator that oozed smoke and presumably kept the *cerveza* cold. There were quite a few empty bottles in the corners, and the walls were thickly plastered with old Wanted posters. Some of the posters were 20 years old. It didn't make me feel any better knowing that these comic opera cops had snapped me up in one day without benefit of poster, while all those peons had been running loose for two decades.

Beyond the brief flare of efficiency which had landed me there, it was obvious that the whole set-up was run in a shockingly cavalier manner. The place didn't even have cells. Instead, there was a high-walled courtyard, 30-feet square, with a lean-to affair in one corner where you could get out of the weather to some extent. There were three Mexican lawbreakers being held prisoner in the courtyard when I was escorted into it. All three of them were standing on top of the lean-to, chatting with friends on the other side of the wall.

Although the conditions were crude and the security would have driven an American corrections administrator to self-immolation, this was the most humane and the most effective jail I've ever been in; perhaps because imprisonment doesn't carry the stigma that it does in the States. Going to jail for a friendly brawl or for a careless theft is looked

238

upon as a natural part of the game of life, not as an occasion to destroy whatever is decent in a man. And imprisonment in Mexico is never reason for a man to lose his family. As often as not, in fact, the family moves right in with him.

Every evening, for instance, our courtyard was overrun by wives, sisters, brothers, children, cousins, and relatives beyond description. These people not only brought in food and cooked meals, they also hauled in quantities of craft material so that my three fellow prisoners could manufacture knicknacks for the tourist trade to pay off their fines and help support their families. As fine and sensible a system as you could ask for.

This jail, as do most other Mexican lockups, also had a room set aside where prisoners could enjoy a bit of privacy with wives and sweethearts. To the extent that they encourage conjugal visiting, Mexico is an eminently civilized country. And, unlike the United States, they have almost no homosexuality problem in their jails and prisons. No little boys being raped by wolf packs, no knife fights over the attentions of a mincing faggot, and no bloody "lover's" quarrels. The wives of Mexican prisoners have no occasion to stray, and they are not punished with years of continence for the crimes of their husbands.

Ah, but these United States of ours. With a single exception — poor, backward Mississippi — conjugal visits are regarded as the grossest of immorality. The very clergymen who condemn the practice as a coddling of prisoners and as a black sin against the Almighty find no moral objection to throwing a downy-cheeked lad into a prison full of older, sex-hungry convicts. Jesus God! To be judged by people who consider forcible homosexuality a more wholesome thing than normal relations between man and woman.

My experience with Mexican jurisprudence was brief.

239

During my one appearance in court I could only catch an occasional word of what was being said, and I wasn't invited to take the stand either for questioning or to testify in my own behalf. My Mexican lawyer was a dapper man with a shiny black mustache, and he seemed to be handling things competently. In any case, I had no choice but to trust him. Now and then he would turn to me and whisper a few words of English, hurried words that told me nothing about the proceedings and seemed intended only to put me at ease. They did not. He was voluble enough in Spanish, however. He strutted up and down before the judge, waving his arms, gnashing his teeth, alternately weeping and spitting fire. Three shades lighter, and they would have loved him in Georgia.

For me, this Mexican trial was a battle of gestures. They were the same gestures I'd seen many times in American courtrooms without really taking any notice, but now they were all I had to go by, and I found them amazingly explicit. When my lawyer felt called upon to point me out to the judge while making some telling point, he would extend his arm in my direction with the palm-up, open-handed gesture of a supplicant. He did this rather too often, I thought. The prosecutor, for his part, showed no such namby-pamby weakness. He stormed across the floor to where I was sitting and boldly thrust his index finger into my face. It was a most expressive finger. It trembled with rage and indignation. It shook violently in the throes of accusation. The prosecutor gestured continually. Even when he was at the bench addressing the judge, his thumb kept jerking back over his shoulder in my direction. And when his assistants brought in the evidence against me — four crates of BARs — his two hands were hardly sufficient for the pointing and accusing.

240

The trial lasted just under an hour and a half. I could tell it was over, because the judge and the prosecutor and my lawyer began shaking hands with one another and telling jokes as they stuffed various papers back into their brief cases. Almost as an afterthought, my lawyer came over to me and said, "You are sentenced to one year in the federal penitentiary. Don't worry."

Then he smiled and shook my hand and walked out of the courtroom, arm in arm with the prosecutor.

Contrary to advice of counsel, I was worried. As it turned out, I didn't need to be, because I was free within a week. But just at that moment I was absolutely convinced that I'd been sold up the river, and I would gladly have strangled that supplicating little weasel of a lawyer.

Notwithstanding that I could have escaped from their crummy little jail anytime I chose, the authorities now decided that I was a very dangerous *hombre*. Before putting me in the car for the transfer to the federal penitentiary, they trussed me up with a good 20 feet of belly chains and leg chains. Shorter chains led from my handcuffs to a couple of very stout uniformed officers, one on either side of me. Most of the Mexicans I'd met so far had been cheerful and talkative, but these two chaps didn't say one word all the time they were with me. It didn't seem a very encouraging start for what I thought was going to be a year in a Mexican prison.

Not that the federal penitentiary itself was anything like encouraging. This was a bleak fortress of a place on the outskirts of Mexico City, popularly known as the Black Palace of Lecumberri. It was home-sweet-home to 4,000 of the toughest, most treacherous thieves and murderers in Mexico — and to me. Well, for five days it was home. On the morning of the sixth day, my lawyer showed up at the

241

gates with a lovely legal document known as an *amparo*. This is a rather peculiar Mexican writ, a legal fruit salad concocted from habeas corpus, show cause, stay of execution, court injunction, and elements of Blackstone and the Napoleonic Code. So long as one is covered by it, no arrest can be made or judgement executed. In this instance, my lawyer had found a judge who agreed that I should not be subjected to imprisonment until it was established that an injustice had not been committed upon me. He issued the *amparo* and I was a free man.

It's unfortunate, really, that I couldn't have spent another week in the Black Palace, as I hardly had a chance to get to know the place. A great deal of my time was spent in a singularly dark and filthy cell, and I wasn't allowed to move around enough to see what the rest of the prison looked like. I should point out, though, that the condition of my cell was not typical of the entire penitentiary. The men there are allowed to furnish them with various personal belongings — everything from chairs and tables and pictures on the wall to weekend señoritas. Had I been there longer, these same amenities would have been available to me.

I had just one noteworthy experience in the Black Palace. I was watching two men play chess one afternoon, and when the game ended one of the men asked me in perfect English if I would like to play. I told him sure, and I sat down and began setting up the pieces, all the while taking a good look at the fellow across the board. He had a squarish, pleasant-looking face and deep, penetrating eyes set-off with horn-rimmed glasses. He looked as though he might have been an insurance salesman, or perhaps a lawyer. He didn't ask me any questions during the game and I didn't ask him any. But he told me his name was Jacques Mornard, so I assumed he was a Frenchman who had somehow run

242

afoul of Mexican law. It was only after I'd been released from the Black Palace that I learned that Jacques Mornard was the assumed name of Ramon Mercader, the man who had assassinated Leon Trotsky.

CHAPTER NINETEEN ·

I sincerely hope that no one ever makes me a gift of a reliable map pinpointing a cache of Aztec treasure, or showing where Maximillian stashed a fortune; I almost pray that some chap won't come running up to me, spouting intelligence of contemporary, south-of-the-border riches to be had for the taking, the score to end all scores in Mexico City, or the whereabouts of an abandoned trunkful of Acapulco gold hidden near La Paz. Because I will have none of it. The *amparo* had made me a free man, temporarily, and I made that freedom permanent by hying my gringo tail out of the country. And I don't intend to return.

Back in Detroit, though; back in the Brown Bottle, with its new management and its respectable businessman clientele, and after the action of the past hectic months, things seemed rather flat. I wasn't even wanted by the local law. And all of my old associates seemed to have been scattered to the winds. Harry Zelnick was doing a 20-year bit in a Federal pen; Big Pastrami had died the year before of ptomaine poisoning; Blind Tony was tending bar at a country club.

It was a dry and empty thing, sitting there wondering where all the thieves had gone. Well could I imagine how the last dodo on the island of Mauritius must have felt; the last, lonely Indian of Tierra del Fuego; the last of the Red-Hot Mamas. It was almost enough to turn a man honest.

But I wouldn't do that. I'd had money before that I'd earned from honest jobs — and I used to hesitate before spending the stuff. I even worried how I was going to make it last, and all that bit, exactly like a Rotarian or a staunch P.T.A. man. And that's not how it was supposed to be with money. Stolen money was much better. It wasn't mine, anyway, so what the hell did I care how fast it went. When it ran out, I could always get more; and I didn't have to worry about finance companies or winding up deep in time payments.

So I wouldn't give up the hustles. I had crawled too long through the loopholes of society — a society where they arrest you for spitting on the sidewalk, but do nothing if you puke on it. I had spent too much time searching diligently for the big score and praying fervently that I wouldn't get pinched, in the meantime, for something small, ridiculous, and unworthy.

It was in this frame of mind that I received a letter from Marlene. She was now in Las Vegas, working with Leda — dear, sweet Leda, who was such a talented and tasteful girl. Every john in the world was in Las Vegas, she said, and they all but knocked you down and forced their money on you. It was the Big Rock Candy Mountain of crime, and all the hustlers were getting rich. Leda and Marlene were knocking down $200 an evening — or at least they had been knocking it down until their swan died from a rare

245

case of cygnus captivus. But that's where the money was, alright alright. And would I like to become a partner by doing them one small favor? You bet!

That same night, I was on my way to Las Vegas — fervently praying I would not suffer the disgrace of getting pinched on a charge of transporting a swan across state lines for immoral purposes.